Literacy Skills
Workbook
for post-primary English

Edited by Martin Kieran & Frances Rocks

GILL EDUCATION

Gill Education

Hume Avenue

Park West

Dublin 12

www.gilleducation.ie

Gill Education is an imprint of M.H. Gill & Co.

© Martin Kieran and Frances Rocks 2015

978 07171 68323

Design by Carole Lynch

The paper used in this book is made from the wood pulp of managed forests. For every tree felled, at least one tree is planted, thereby renewing natural resources.

For permission to reproduce poetry, the authors and publisher gratefully acknowledge the following: 'Balloon Fiesta' by Moira Andrew used with permission of the author; extract from 'Homework' by Russell Hoban taken from *Egg Thoughts: And Other Frances Songs*, published by Faber & Faber, used with permission; 'What is the Sun?' by Wes Magee, from *The Very Best of Wes Magee*, published by Macmillan Children's Books in 2001; Seamus Heaney extracts, 'The Forge' from *Door into the Dark* (1969), 'A Constable Calls' from *North* (1975), 'Postscript' from *The Spirit Level* (1996), 'Mossbawn: Sunlight' from *North*, 'Bogland' from *Door into the Dark* and 'The Tollund Man' from *Wintering Out* (1972), all published by Faber & Faber.

The author and publisher have made every effort to trace all copyright holders, but if any has been inadvertently overlooked we would be pleased to make the necessary arrangement at the first opportunity.

CONTENTS

Introduction

English is a 'living language'. It keeps changing and evolving over time. There are many differences between the English we speak and the English we write.

Standard English follows definite grammar, punctuation and spelling rules – and it's best to use these rules in most cases. Of course, there are always exceptions to the rules. Informal, non-standard English (such as slang, colloquialisms and abbreviations) also has a place in our daily conversation or text messaging.

Using grammar, punctuation and spelling correctly in your writing is essential for clear communication. This workbook will help you to practise and perfect these vital skills. It will ensure that what you write is more easily understood and enjoyable to read. You can improve your language skills by working through this book and completing the written exercises.

It is also important that you read as much and as widely as possible – books, magazines, newspapers, comics, graphic novels, etc. By doing so, you will be building up your store of words and discovering how they can be constructed in many and varied ways.

Using a dictionary and thesaurus can also be very helpful. By taking good care when you write and by reading in your own time and for your own pleasure, you will develop a clearer understanding of how language works and gain greater confidence in using written English yourself.

Throughout this book, there are written exercises to help you understand and correctly apply what you learn. You'll see regular 'Learning Outcomes' which summarise what you have studied, as well as a space for your signature when you have completed each chapter. At the end of each of the four main sections, there is a space for your teacher to sign as well.

We hope you enjoy using this skills workbook and improving your understanding of the exciting language that is English!

Martin Kieran &
Frances Rocks

Section 1 – Grammar

» Nouns

A noun is a word used to name a **person**, **place**, **thing**, **animal**, or **quality**.

Common Nouns

Common nouns are the names of any **ordinary** (common) thing that we can see, taste or touch.

We need to name things in order to communicate with each other and understand the world around us.

Examples:

boy, girl, city, town, car, train dog, cat

Written work

Re-write the following, underlining all the nouns.

(The first one is already done for you.)

I am not saying my <u>mum</u> is a bad cook – but the cake she baked for the cake sale at the school open day was a disaster! It looked like the cat sat on it. My dad laughed and laughed.

_____

_____

_____

_____

_____

_____

Written work

What is the common noun for someone who …?

(Fill in the blanks. The first one is already done for you.)

investigates crime	*detective*
treats sick people	
paints pictures	
lends books	
writes for a newspaper	
plays soccer	

Proper Nouns

A **proper noun** is used to name a particular **person**, **place**, **animal** or **thing**.

They always start with a capital letter. Without these proper nouns, we wouldn't even have a name!

> Another name for a capital letter is an 'uppercase' letter. Small letters are called 'lowercase' letters.

Examples:

John, Mary, Dublin, Cork, Lassie, September

Written work

Re-write the following, underlining all the proper nouns.

(The first one is already done for you.)

On a <u>Sunday</u> afternoon in May at the Tara Hotel in Galway, my phone rings. It's my best friend Barry Murphy's dad, Cormac. He wonders if Barry is with me. He hasn't answered his phone, which is not like Barry. I quickly text Conor, another friend of Barry's, to see if he has any news.

Written work

Re-write the names of these famous writers using the rule for proper nouns.

charles dickens _____

j.k. rowling _____

roddy doyle _____

william shakespeare _____

jacqueline wilson _____

Collective Nouns

A **collective noun** refers to a **collection** or group of items.

Examples:

a *class* of students, a *team* of footballers, a *flock* of birds, a *herd* of animals

Written work

Re-write the following sentences, filling in the blanks with one of the collective nouns listed below.

(The first one is already done for you.)

wad, bouquet, swarm, litter, suite, bunch

1. The boy was badly stung by a _____ of bees while on holiday.

   The boy was badly stung by a swarm of bees while on holiday.

2. The millionaire took a _____ of notes from his wallet and gave the waiter a generous tip.

   _____

3. Tommy gave Lucy a _____ of flowers and a _____ of grapes yesterday.

   _____

4. The little girl found it hard to choose just one puppy from the _____.

   _____

5. The famous actor booked a _____ of rooms at the Ritz Hotel.

   _____

Abstract Nouns

An **abstract noun** refers to feelings or ideas.

Examples:

happiness, sadness, beauty, freedom

Written work

Re-write the following short speech, underlining all the abstract nouns.

(The first one is already done for you.)

> Friends, ask yourselves this. What is <u>**freedom**</u>? Isn't it just fantasy? Those of us who believe in such foolish ideas as equality will be disappointed. Dreaming is a waste of time. You will end up full of anger and sadness.

Written work

Place the following nouns in the correct column.

Kilkenny, hamster, car, choir, happiness, Wednesday, jacket, hunger, flock, city, gang, laptop, Ellen, anger, Waterford, table, Paul, library, beauty, baby, poverty, herd, electricity, cheese, Co. Leitrim, detention, Macbeth, crop, snow, Taoiseach, team, fear, bunch, suspicion

Common Noun	Proper Noun	Collective Noun	Abstract Noun

Learning Outcomes

I have studied nouns.

- A common noun is a word that names a person, place, thing or idea.

- Proper nouns name a particular person, place or thing.

- Collective nouns refer to groups of people or things.

- Abstract nouns usually refer to feelings and ideas.

Student signature	**Date**

» Pronouns

A pronoun is used in place of a noun. Pronouns add variety to writing and prevent it from becoming repetitive.

Examples:

he, she, it, them, there, us, him

Pronouns can **replace** nouns, as a means of avoiding repetition.

Mike loves football. Mike plays football most weekends. → **Repetitive**

Mike loves football. He plays it most weekends. → **Fluent**

Written work

Re-write each of the following sentences, replacing the nouns with the appropriate pronouns.

(The first one is already done for you.)

1. Mrs Murray gave the stray cat some food and treated the cat well.

   Mrs Murray gave the stray cat some food and treated it well.

2. The vet tried to make the dog's owner give the dog regular exercise.

   _____

3. John cycles to school because John wants to be fit and healthy.

   _____

4. Don't take your old jacket with you; take your new jacket.

   _____

5. Annie brought her camera to London – Annie just loves taking pictures.

   _____

Subject and Object Pronouns

Subject pronouns are the main pronouns: *I, you, he, she, it, we* and *they*.

They usually come at the start of the sentence and perform the action of the verb.

So instead of: *Sarah was looking for her pencil case,*
it would be: *She was looking for her pencil case.*

An **object pronoun** acts as the object of the sentence – the verb is done *to* them.

Object pronouns are *me, you, him, her, it, us* and *them*.

Example: Sean gave *me* an apple.

> 'Me' is the object pronoun because the action of the verb [which in this case is 'giving'] is being done to 'me'.

Written work

Re-write the following sentences using the correct pronoun from the brackets.

(The first one is already done for you.)

1. Uncle Ted gave (*we, us*) a book about old Hollywood movies.

   Uncle Ted gave **us** a book about old Hollywood movies.

2. (*He, Him*) and his entire family just love films.

   _____

3. Siobhan and (*I, me*) are both good tennis players.

   _____

4. I wish you could see (*us, we*) play sometime.

   _____

5. Our parents say we make (*they, them*) proud.

   _____

Using 'I' or 'me'

An easy way to know whether you use 'I' or 'me' in a sentence is to write or say the sentence just with the 'I' or 'me' part and see if it makes sense. So for example, should it be 'Emma and I went to the cinema yesterday' or 'Emma and me went to the cinema yesterday'. Take Emma out of it, and see if the sentence makes sense on its own: 'I went to the cinema'/'me went to the cinema'. So in this instance, 'I' is correct. Now what about 'Mum took Fergal and I/me to the shop' – again, take Fergal out of it and see which makes sense: 'Mum took I to the shop'/ 'Mum took me to the shop'. Here, 'me' is correct.

Possessive Pronouns

Possessive pronouns are used in place of nouns.

They include the following:

my, mine, our, ours, its, his, her, hers, their, theirs, your, yours, whose, one's

All of these words demonstrate **ownership**.

Example: That old house is *theirs* and its paint is flaking.

Written work

Re-write the following sentences, underlining the possessive pronouns.

(The first one is already done for you.)

1. That new house on the corner is ours.

   That new house on the corner is <u>ours</u>.

2. Whose book is on the desk?

3. The money was really theirs for the taking.

4. We shall finally have what is rightfully ours.

5. I never did find out whose phone number that was.

6. What's mine is yours, my friend.

Whose and who's

Be careful not to confuse 'whose' and 'who's' when writing.

'Whose' is a possessive pronoun:

Whose *diaries are those?* ➜ possessive pronoun
Here 'whose' is possessive, meaning the diaries belonging to someone.

'Who's' is a contraction (contraction means a shortened form of a word or words):

Who's *that at the front door?* ➜ contraction
Here 'who's' means 'who is', with the apostrophe (') standing in place of the missing 'i' in 'is'. We'll learn more about contractions when we come to talk about apostrophes on p. 57.

Written work

Re-write the following sentences correctly, by selecting *whose* or *who's* from the brackets.

(The first one is already done for you.)

1. I would like to find out (*whose, who's*) talking at the back of the class.

   I would like to find out **who's** talking at the back of the class.

2. It's hard to decide (*whose, who's*) fancy-dress costume is the best.

   _____

3. We're not sure (*whose, who's*) coming to the cinema tonight.

   _____

4. I wonder (*whose, who's*) books have been left on the table.

   _____

5. Tell me (*whose, who's*) iPad was damaged and (*whose, who's*) going to pay for the repair.

   _____

Reflexive Pronouns

A **reflexive pronoun** usually refers to the subject of a sentence.

myself, yourself, himself, herself, itself, ourselves, themselves

Example: Paul found *himself* alone in the train station.

Written work

Re-write the following sentences, underlining the reflective pronouns.

(The first one is already done for you.)

1. Jane needed to be by herself for a short time.

   Jane needed to be by **herself** for a short time.

2. The boys made themselves beans on toast.

   _____

3. Ben burnt himself when he used the grill.

   _____

4. The dog dried itself off by rolling around on the lawn.

_____

5. Do you ever need to be by yourself?

_____

Indefinite Pronouns

An **indefinite pronoun** does not refer to a particular person, place or thing – it's not very definite!

everyone, everybody, many, most, few, each, some, all, nobody, no one

Example: _Everyone_ is making too much noise.

Indefinite pronouns can be **singular** or **plural**.

Examples:

Everyone on the bus was feeling unwell.

Some of the boys are missing.

Written work

Re-write the following sentences, underlining the indefinite pronouns.

(The first one is already done for you.)

1. Most students are quite neat and tidy.

<u>Most</u> students are quite neat and tidy

2. Every school needs to be careful about litter.

_____

3. If each person helps, there shouldn't be many problems.

_____

4. Is anybody prepared to volunteer?

_____

5. All of us want a clean environment.

_____

Relative Pronouns

Relative pronouns are used to connect a clause or phrase to a noun or pronoun, giving extra information about that noun or pronoun.

who, which, that, whom, whose, where, when

> A 'clause' is a group of related words containing a subject and a verb, while a 'phrase' is usually two or more related words within a sentence.

The main relative pronouns are **who**, **which** and **that**.
Use **who** for people and **which** or **that** for things.

Examples:

This is the new phone *which* I bought last week.
Can I have the ruler *that* I gave you this morning?
Do you know the boy *who* started in First Year last week?

> ## Tip!
> ### Knowing when to use *who* and *whom*
> If you ever find yourself confused by whether to use *who* or *whom*, try slotting in *he/him* or *they/them* to see if the sentence still makes sense. *He* or *they* would mean you should use *who*, and *him* or *them* would mean that *whom* is the correct choice. (Hint to remember: both *him* and *them* end in *m*, like *whom*, so that would be the one to use!) For a question, you might need to use the answer, and other sentences might need rearranging for the trick to work.
>
> *To whom am I speaking?* (I am speaking to him)
> *Who left the fridge door open again?* (He left the fridge door open again)

Written work

Re-write the following sentences, underlining the relative pronouns.
(The first one is already done for you.)

1. Do you know the teacher who just walked by?

   Do you know the teacher <u>who</u> just walked by?

2. My mum's company, which makes mobile phones, is moving to Cork.

   _____

3. Can I have the pen that I gave you this morning?

   _____

4. I like visiting places where there is plenty to do.

   _____

5. The child whose kitten was lost is very upset.

   _____

Learning Outcomes

I have studied some of the main pronouns.

- A pronoun does the same job as a noun, and can be used instead of nouns.

- They prevent writing from becoming too repetitive.

- There are many different types of pronouns: subject, object, possessive, reflexive, indefinite, relative.

Student signature	*Date*

» Articles

Articles are small words that go before nouns. The most important articles are 'the', 'a' and 'an'.

'The', 'A' and 'An'

'The' is called the **definite article**.

'I am going to *the* party tonight' – you are going to a definite, specific party.

'A' or 'An' is called the **indefinite article**.

'I am going to *a* party tonight' – you are going to a party, but you're not definite (indefinite) which one you are going to go to.

So, the meaning of a sentence can change depending on whether you use the definite ('the') or indefinite ('a'/'an') article. They show whether a noun (in this instance, 'party') is specific (*the* party) or general (*a* party).

Using 'A' or 'An'

Use 'an' before words beginning with a vowel (there are five letters which are vowels: a, e, i, o, u), e.g. *an* ice-cream, *an* actor, *an* elephant.

Use 'a' before words beginning with a consonant (all the letters that are not vowels) e.g. *a* book, *a* circus, *a* panda.

However, watch out for exceptions to the rule, such as words that sound as though they begin with a 'y' – e.g. *a* university, *a* European country. (It would be very cumbersome anyhow to say 'an university' or 'an European country' – try it!) Other exceptions include words where the 'h' is silent – *an* hour, *an* honour. (Again, try saying them out loud with 'a'.)

Written work

Re-write the following sentences, using the correct indefinite articles from the brackets.

1. Laurie hopes to become (*a, an*) actress when she finishes her studies.

   _____

2. The film had (*a, an*) happy ending.

   _____

3. The patient needed to be rushed to (*a, an*) hospital.

   _____

4. It was so wet that Mum had to buy (*a, an*) umbrella.

   _____

5. There was (*a, an*) accident on the motorway today.

   _____

6. I'd really love (*a, an*) piece of cake.

   _____

7. Mark saw (*a, an*) elephant in Dublin Zoo.

   _____

8. Our teacher told us a story about (*a, an*) unicorn.

   _____

9. Eve really wants (*a, an*) dog for Christmas.

   _____

10. Leo has (*a, an*) unusual hobby.

    _____

Learning Outcomes

I have studied the rules for using articles.

- There are two articles in the English language: *the* and *a/an*.
- The definite article *the* is used to refer to specific nouns.
- The indefinite articles *a* and *an* are used with non-particular nouns.
- In most cases, we use *a* with words beginning with a consonant.
- We usually use *an* with words beginning with a vowel.

Student signature _____   *Date* _____

» Adjectives

An adjective is a 'describing' word.

Adjectives are words that **describe or modify (change) a person or thing in a sentence**.

Adjectives **describe** a noun or pronoun.

Examples: the *green* grass, the *lonely* man, the *cold* river, *two* boys, *clever* students

Adjectives tell us **what something is like:**

- what it looks like
- how big it is
- how many there are.

Adjectives **answer the questions:**

- What kind is it?
- How many are there?
- Which one is it?

Adjectives are placed **before** or **after** the noun or pronoun. They add descriptive and interesting detail to your writing.

Written work

Complete the following sentences by choosing a suitable adjective from the list given below.

(The first one is already done for you.)

skipping, kitchen, beach, blue, injured, black

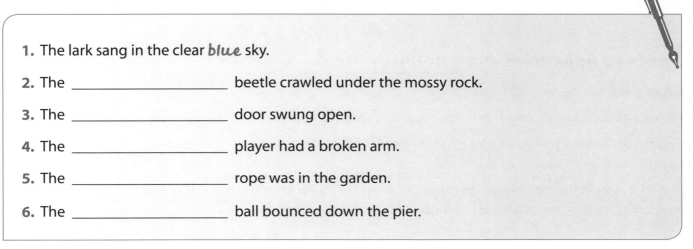

1. The lark sang in the clear *blue* sky.

2. The _____ beetle crawled under the mossy rock.

3. The _____ door swung open.

4. The _____ player had a broken arm.

5. The _____ rope was in the garden.

6. The _____ ball bounced down the pier.

Written work

Re-write the passage below, underlining all the adjectives.

(The first one is already done for you.)

The <u>lonely</u> woman sat on her own night after night. Her old husband always went to the local pub. She decided to teach him a terrifying lesson. She cut two holes in a white sheet. She ran down to the abandoned church and waited. Her tipsy husband came along. She pulled the sheet over her head and began to scream. Her husband smiled. 'Have you come out on this cold night to walk me home, old ghost?' he cheerfully remarked.

Forming adjectives from nouns

Adjectives can be formed from nouns.

For example, the noun *anger* can become the adjective *angry*.

Anger filled the man when he looked at the dent in his car. (Here 'anger' is an abstract noun – a feeling or idea.)

The angry goalkeeper thumped the goalpost when the striker scored. (Now we've made it into an adjective – describing what sort of mood the goalkeeper was in.)

Written work

Form adjectives from the following nouns.

(The first one is already done for you.)

Noun	Adjective
Hero	heroic
sun	
music	
beauty	
Ireland	
strength	

Possessive Adjectives

Possessive adjectives are used to show ownership or belonging.

my, your, its, his, her, their

Example: The girl loved *her* puppy.

> ## Note!
>
> A possessive pronoun can be used in place of a noun – e.g. 'Joe's hoodie is green. Mine is blue.' A possessive adjective, on the other hand, describes a noun and is placed before the noun – e.g. 'I think my phone is cooler than her phone.'

Written work

Choose the correct possessive adjective from the list to complete the sentences below.

(The first one is already done for you.)

my, your, its, his, their

1. I love **my** weekends.

2. The boy lifted _____ schoolbag into the car.

3. The children couldn't wait for _____ school holidays to begin.

4. _____ tea is ready,' Mum called.

5. The cat licked _____ paw.

Written work

Underline the possessive adjectives in the following sentences.

(The first one is already done for you.)

1. I did it <u>my</u> way.

2. Our ice-cream is the best.

3. Your country needs you.

4. It is all my own work.

5. The birds build their nests in spring.

6. The lion shook its mane.

Demonstrative Adjectives

Demonstrative adjectives point out something in particular.

this, that, these, those

Example: *This* is the book I want.

Written work

Underline the demonstrative adjectives in the following sentences.

(The first one is already done for you.)

1. <u>That</u> answer won't do.

2. These are the worst jokes yet.

3. Those were the days.

4. I like this pair of trainers.

5. Are these your half-eaten chocolates?

Interrogative Adjectives

Interrogative adjectives ask a question (they **_interrogate_**).

which, whose, what

Example: *Which answer is the right one?*

Written work

Underline the interrogative adjectives in the following sentences.

(The first one is already done for you.)

1. <u>Whose</u> iPad is this?

2. What kind of a singer are you?

3. What are you doing?

4. Which of you broke the window?

Comparative and Superlative Adjectives

Adjectives are often used to **compare** and **distinguish** things from each other.

George is *tall.*

Henry is *taller* than George.

Tom is the *tallest* of them all.

Comparative adjectives compare two things and are formed by adding *-er* to the adjective: *Henry is **taller** than George.* (We are *comparing* the heights of the two boys.)

Superlative adjectives compare three things or more and are formed by adding *-est* to the adjective: *Tom is the **tallest** of them all.*

> 'Superlative' (say: *su-purr-la-tiv*) actually means 'of the highest quality or degree', hence a 'superlative' adjective, an adjective pointing out the most extreme degree.

Written work

Form the comparative and superlative forms from the following adjectives.

(The first one is already done for you.)

Adjective	Comparative	Superlative
big	bigger	biggest
hot		
cold		
bright		
sharp		
long		

Note!

There are (as always in English!) some exceptions to this rule.

Adjective	Comparative	Superlative
many	more	most
good	better	best
little	less	least
bad	worse	worst

Written work

Re-write the following dialogue using the correct form of the adjective in brackets.

(The first one is already done for you.)

Neil: This is the (bad) film I've ever seen.

This is the **worst** film I've ever seen.

Joe: It could have been so much (good).

_____

Neil: It was the (long) film ever!

_____

Joe: Don't exaggerate! We saw a (long) one last week.

_____

Written work

Underline the adjectives in the following sports headlines.

(The first one is already done for you. Note that there may be more than one adjective in some headlines.)

1. An <u>outstanding</u> star shines in the galaxy.

2. Red card makes it sweet and sour for Cork.

3. Slow start costs Munster.

4. Gritty Ulster earn lifeline.

5. Composed Connacht team deserve certain win.

6. Fierce resistance breaks Leinster's tight hold.

Learning Outcomes

I have studied adjectives.

- An adjective describes a noun or pronoun.

- It is placed before or after the noun or pronoun.

- Adjectives can be formed from nouns.

- Possessive adjectives denote the owner of something.

- Demonstrative adjectives point out something in particular.

- Interrogative adjectives ask a question.

- Comparative and superlative adjectives compare adjectives.

Student signature   **Date**

» Verbs

A verb is a 'doing' or 'being' word.

Verbs are usually **action** words.

Every sentence needs at least one verb; they even allow you to create a one-word sentence: **'Go!'**

Examples:

We *went* to the shops.

Lucy *is* so angry.

I *slept* in late on Saturday.

Jack *thinks* too much.

Written work

Re-write each of the following sentences, underlining all the verbs.

(The first one is already done for you.)

1. Jason is a very talented guitarist.

   <u>Jason **is** a very talented guitarist.</u>

2. Mrs Murphy sells fresh fruit in the local market.

   _____

3. The centre forward aimed straight for the net.

   _____

4. Meg guessed the correct answer.

   _____

5. The rain fell heavily.

   _____

Tip!

An easy way to check if a word is a verb or not is, if you can put *I, you, he, she, they* or *it*, in front of it, and it makes sense, then the word is a verb!

Verbs appear in many forms. For example, the verb *sing* can be: *sing, sings, sang, sung, singing.*

Verbs can be **active** (*The goalkeeper made a terrific save*) or **passive** (*A terrific save was made by the goalkeeper*).

Written work

Re-write each of the following sentences, underlining all the active and passive verbs.

(The first one is already done for you.)

1. The shop window was smashed by the thief.

   The shop window <u>was smashed</u> by the thief.

2. The cherry tree grew very tall.

3. Conor wore his awesome hoodie.

4. The seal balanced the beach ball on its nose.

5. The postman was bitten by our neighbour's dog.

Verbs can have **more than one part**.

A verb often consist of a single word (*The ball* **flew** *through the air*), but verbs can have more than one part. These are sometimes called **verb phrases**.

Examples:

The caretaker *cut down* the tree.

Dad wants me to *cut back on* sugary drinks.

Our teacher is *always forgetting* his diary.

Who *came up with* the idea of grammar?

Verbs must **agree** with the **subject** of the sentence.

To find out the subject of the sentence, look at the verb (the action word) and ask who or what is doing the action. This is the subject of the sentence, and it is with this that the verb must agree. If one (single) person or thing is doing the action, then the verb must also be singular.

Example: The child *is* feeling ill. (There is only one child, hence the verb 'is' instead of 'are'.)

If more than one person or thing is doing the action, then the verb must be plural.

Example: All of the children *are* feeling ill. (All the children are ill, hence the verb 'are' instead of 'is'.)

Written work

Re-write the following sentences by selecting the correct verb from the brackets.

(The first one is already done for you.)

1. Pat and Claire (*was, were*) cycling along the path.

   Pat and Claire **were** cycling along the path.

2. One of the classroom windows (*has, have*) been left open.

3. The man with all the big dogs (*walks, walk*) down my street.

4. Sara and her friends (*is, are*) out shopping again.

5. Either my mum or dad (*is, are*) going to collect me.

Note!

Collective nouns (e.g. *team, staff, family, choir* – 'collections' of people) are usually considered singular, so the verb must also be in the singular.

Examples:
The crowd *is* becoming very annoyed. (not 'are')
Our family *has* a very long history. (not 'have')
The Irish rugby team *is* world-famous. (not 'are')

Verb Tenses

Verbs can show **when something is happening**.

They can be in the **present tense** (*is happening right now*).

Example: The girls *are walking* to school.

They can be in the **past tense** (*has already happened*).

Example: They *walked* to school yesterday.

They can be in the **future tense** (*has yet to happen*).

Example: They *will walk* to school tomorrow.

Written work

Re-write the following sentences and then label them *past, present* or *future*.

(The first one is already done for you.)

1. Don works in his garden every afternoon.

   <u>Don works in his garden every afternoon.</u> **Present**

2. Last week, he prepared the soil for planting lettuce.

   _____

3. He will pull out weeds next weekend.

   _____

4. He really enjoys being outdoors.

   _____

5. The garden will soon be full of vegetables.

   _____

Transitive and Intransitive Verbs

A **transitive verb** is what we call a verb that is followed by a noun or pronoun that *receives* the action.

Example: Jane *baked some muffins*.

So in this instance, the object – the muffins – is receiving the action of the verb – they are being baked.

Other examples:

Sean *kicked* Peter under the table.

I *moved* the chair.

Moya *painted* a colourful picture.

An **intransitive verb** is what we call a verb that does not have an object receiving the action.

Example: The kitten *purred*.

So in this instance the action of the kitten – purring – has no object – the kitten is just purring for the sake of it!

Other examples:

I *laughed*.

The book *fell*.

The horse *galloped*.

Written work

Re-write the following sentences and then label the verbs *transitive* or *intransitive*.

(The first one is already done for you.)

1. Next year, Mike will run his first marathon.

   <u>Next year, Mike will run his first marathon. Transitive</u>

2. Jamie told a joke.

   _____

3. Oliver laughed.

   _____

4. Mary brought a cake to the party.

   _____

5. Duty calls.

   _____

Learning Outcomes

I have studied verbs.

- A verb is an action word.
- A sentence needs to have at least one verb.
- Verbs show what is happening in a sentence.
- There are many different types of verbs.
- Verbs can have more than one part.

Student signature _____ **Date** _____

» Adverbs

An adverb usually gives more information about a verb.

Adding 'ly'

Adverbs are often formed by **adding 'ly' to an adjective**.

Examples:

sad → sadly

brave → bravely

slow → slowly

You will often recognise an adverb because many of them end in 'ly'.

Examples:

Patrick arrived *early*.

Ciara *suddenly* appeared.

Written work

Form adverbs from the adjectives listed below.

(The first one is already done for you.)

1. deep → *deeply*

2. soft → _____

3. clear → _____

4. light → _____

5. bright → _____

6. warm → _____

Exceptions!

Adjectives that end in 'y' form the adverb by changing the 'y' to an 'i' and adding 'ly'.

Examples:

pretty ➜ prettily

lazy ➜ lazily

Written work

Form adverbs from the following adjectives.

(The first one is already done for you.)

1. angry ➜ *angrily*

2. hungry ➜ _____

3. heavy ➜ _____

4. hasty ➜ _____

5. crazy ➜ _____

6. merry ➜ _____

Adjectives that end in 'le' form the adverb by dropping the final letter and adding 'y'.

Example: simple ➜ simply

Written work

Form adverbs from the following adjectives.

(The first one is already done for you.)

1. terrible ➜ *terribly*

2. double ➜ _____

3. justifiable ➜ _____

4. incredible ➜ _____

5. unbelievable ➜ _____

6. comfortable ➜ _____

Written work

Re-write the passage below, circling all the adverbs you find in it.

The heavy stone had been dumped in the village square long ago. Yesterday I decided to climb on top of it. Nervously, I started to pick at the green moss which grew thickly all over it. Suddenly I saw some letters. They said, 'Turn me around.' Furiously, I pulled and heaved. Perhaps it marked buried treasure. I scratched my hands painfully as I hauled and shoved. Gradually, the stone moved. I saw more writing. It said, 'Right way up.'

_____

_____

_____

_____

_____

_____

_____

_____

_____

_____

_____

_____

As well as describing verbs, **adverbs can also describe adjectives**. Such adverbs tell us the **extent of an action**.

Examples: very, quite, really

The manager says the team was _very_ unlucky to lose the match.

Other adverbs tell us the **scale of the action**.

Examples: so, too, much, more, most, completely, fairly, utterly

She was _completely_ astounded by the day's events.

Written work

Complete the following sentences, using an adverb from the list.

poorly, nearly, too, fairly, rather, so, really

(The first one is already done for you.)

1. I was **so** bored.

2. I ate _____ much.

3. Our team played _____ and was _____ beaten.

4. I _____ love chocolate.

5. I like chips with vinegar _____ than salt.

6. She is _____ ready to go.

Adverbs can tell us about the **time** of an action.

Example: The band performed the show *twice*.

Written work

Choose a suitable adverb from the list below to complete the sentences.

since, regularly, tomorrow, seldom, now, soon

(The first one is already done for you.)

1. Stop talking **now**!

2. Cathy hoped that the concert would be starting _____ .

3. I am going to the cinema _____ .

4. My friend is living abroad, so we _____ meet now.

5. It's been snowing _____ we arrived.

6. We like swimming, so we go to the pool _____ .

Adverbs can tell us **where** the action takes place.

Example: Put your coat *here*.

Written work

Choose a suitable adverb from the list below to complete the sentences.

abroad, here, back, around, out, everywhere

(The first one is already done for you.)

1. **Here** is the present I promised you.

2. Sophie looked _____ but she couldn't see the taxi.

3. It's late, so I'm going _____ to class.

4. Don't go _____ with her again.

5. _____ was covered in snow.

6. My aunt has been living _____ for several years.

Learning Outcomes

I have studied adverbs.

- An adverb usually tells us about a verb (when, where and how).

- Many adverbs end in 'ly'.

- An adverb can also tell us more about an adjective.

Student signature

Date

» Conjunctions

A conjunction joins parts of a sentence together, or makes two parts of a sentence relate to each other (just like 'or' did there!).

Conjunctions are usually found in the middle of sentences – they link two parts of a sentence. Common conjunctions, such as 'and', 'but' and 'because', link phrases together into longer sentences.

Example: I would love a pet monkey, *but* my dad won't let me.

> Conjunctions are also known as 'connectives', because they 'connect' two parts of a sentence.

Written work

Re-write the following sentences, putting in the missing conjunctions from the list.

if, so, before, and, unlike, because

(The first one is already done for you.)

1. The postman called to our house ...... he had a parcel to deliver.

   The postman called to our house **because** he had a parcel to deliver.

2. There is a rabbit in our garden ...... it is eating the lettuce plants.

3. Lisa put on her pyjamas ...... she went to bed.

4. The children will probably not be allowed out today ...... the weather is bad.

5. The kitten was small and quiet, ... the enormous barking dog.

6. Yesterday it snowed ...... I wore my woolly scarf and warm gloves.

Conjunctions can sometimes be placed **at the start of a sentence**.

Examples:

If it rains tomorrow, Chloe will probably stay in bed.

Because it's so cold, my hands are turning blue!

Conjunctions can be made up of **more than one word**.

Examples:

There are many types of monkey, *for example*, the spider monkey and Tamarin monkey.

I usually prefer to walk *rather than* go by bus.

Written work

Re-write the following sentences, putting in the missing conjunctions from the list.

if, until, or, but, when, in case

(The first one is already done for you.)

1. I'd love to go to the cinema ...... I have to finish my homework first.

   I'd love to go to the cinema but I have to finish my homework first.

2. The match ended ...... the referee blew the final whistle.

   _____

3. I will not talk to her ...... she apologises for what she did.

   _____

4. Do you like pasta ...... do you prefer pizza?

   _____

5. ...... we don't get a break soon, we will all fall asleep.

   _____

6. I brought along some chocolate ...... I get hungry.

   _____

Learning Outcomes

I have studied conjunctions.

- A conjunction joins parts of a sentence together.
- Conjunctions can be one word, or more than one word.
- You can start a sentence with a conjunction, but you shouldn't do it too often as it is not considered best practice.

Student signature   *Date*

_____

» Prepositions

Prepositions are usually very small words. They tell us something about position, place or time.

Examples:

The book is *on* the table. (*position*)

The dog ran *across* the road. (*place*)

During lunchtime students relax. (*time*)

Written work

Re-write the following sentences, inserting prepositions from the list.

from, down, into, through, between, during

(The first one is already done for you.)

1. The boy walked ...... the shop.

   The boy walked *into* the shop.

2. Their mother divided the money ...... Seán and Niamh.

3. The stone was thrown ...... the window.

4. Butter is made ...... milk.

5. The weather is very hot ...... the summer.

6. The stream trickled ...... the hill.

A preposition usually comes **before a noun** to show the noun's relationship to another noun in the sentence.

> The word 'preposition' is from Latin and means 'place in front of'.

Examples:

This is a jug *for* milk. (The preposition *for* shows the relationship between *jug* and *milk*.)

The bird flew *above* the clouds. (The preposition *above* shows the relationship between *clouds* and *flew*.)

Written work

Re-write the following dialogue correctly, replacing the underlined prepositions with correct ones from the list.

of, about, in, to, by, round, on, with

(The first one is already done for you.)

Jack: There's no doubt.

Jill: What are you talking <u>of</u>?

Jack: The warming <u>at</u> the planet, silly!

Jill: And you're suddenly <u>with</u> a position to know!

Jack: Yep! I'm backed <u>on</u> all the most important scientists.

Jill: You can't listen <u>at</u> them. They're <u>up</u> the bend!

Jack: You're just so ignorant <u>from</u> them.

Jill: <u>Over</u> your bike!

Joe: Having a conversation <u>against</u> you is just totally impossible!

Jack: There's no doubt.
Jill: What are you talking **about**?

_____

_____

_____

_____

_____

_____

_____

Ending on a preposition

It used to be considered grammatically incorrect to end a sentence with a preposition. However, adhering to this rule sometimes makes a sentence sound very awkward. So it is nowadays more acceptable to end a sentence with a preposition. Consider this witty quote from Winston Churchill, UK prime minister during the 1940s:

Ending a sentence with a preposition is something up with which I will not put.

Churchill was showing how sticking to this rule made the sentence sound very peculiar. So we generally accept that a preposition is a perfectly appropriate kind of word to end a sentence *with*.

Written work

Re-write the following sentences to end them with a preposition.

1. On what did you step?

_____

2. Up I wish she would cheer.

_____

3. Paid for the dress had not been.

_____

4. Off the match was rained.

_____

5. I think they are foolish on taking this.

_____

Confusing Prepositions!

Some prepositions are occasionally confused with similar-sounding words – particularly 'except'/'accept', and 'past'/'passed'; or used incorrectly – particularly 'between' and 'among'.

EXCEPT and ACCEPT

The word *except* is a preposition and means *not including*.

Example: I know everybody at the party *except* Jennifer.

The word *accept* is a verb and means *agree with* or *receive*.

Example: The criminal will *accept* the jury's decision.

Written work

Re-write the following sentences, choosing *accept* or *except* as appropriate.

(The first one is already done for you.)

1. Nobody will (*accept, except*) that result.

   Nobody will accept that result.

2. I love chocolates, (*accept, except*) the coffee creams.

   _____

3. You will have to (*accept, except*) the situation.

_____

4. I was delighted to (*accept, except*) the invitation.

_____

5. We headed off to Dublin, all (*accept, except*) Betty.

_____

6. When will you (*accept, except*) that I mean no?

_____

PAST and PASSED

The word *past* is a preposition describing *place* and *time*.

Examples:

The horse was first *past* the post.

In the *past*, homes had no electricity.

The word *passed* is an action verb and refers to *the act of passing*.

Examples:

All the students *passed* their English exam.

Áine *passed* the parcel to Anthony.

Written work

Re-write the following sentences, choosing *past* or *passed* as appropriate.

(The first one is already done for you.)

1. He (*past, passed*) the salt and pepper.

He passed the salt and pepper.

2. In the (*past, passed*) there were no mobile phones.

_____

3. The boat sailed (*past, passed*) the waiting crowd.

_____

4. He (*past, passed*) the ball to the striker.

_____

5. The storm (*past, passed*) quickly.

_____

6. The (*past, passed*) is a foreign country.

_____

BETWEEN and AMONG

Between and *among* are both prepositions, **but:**

The word *between* is used when sharing something between two persons or things.

Example: Dad divided the pocket money evenly *between* Lee and Caroline.

The word *among* is generally used when sharing something among more than two people.

Example: The teacher divided the sweets *among* the pupils.

Written work

Re-write the following sentences, choosing *between* or *among* as appropriate.

(The first one is already done for you.)

1. I searched (*between, among*) my things for my passport.
   I searched **among** my things for my passport.

2. The Irish Sea flows (*between, among*) England and Ireland.

_____

3. During the game, I had to sit (*between, among*) a crowd of rival supporters.

_____

4. The secretary left a little space (*between, among*) each word and the next.

_____

5. The triplets seldom agree (*between, among*) themselves.

_____

6. I was shocked to see the space (*between, among*) his two front teeth.

_____

Learning Outcomes

I have studied the rules for prepositions.

- A preposition is a small word which tells about position, place or time.

- It is usually placed before a noun or pronoun to show the relationship with another noun or pronoun in the sentence.

- Prepositions can be easily confused: except/accept, past/passed; or misused: between/among.

Student signature

Date

Teacher's initial

Section 2 – Punctuation

» Capital Letters and End Punctuation

Capitals (also called 'uppercase' letters) are important punctuation marks and come at the beginning of sentences. End punctuation shows when a sentence is finished and gives an indication of what the sentence means.

Capitals

wIThoUt ThE pRoPeR usE oF cAPitAls, sEntENCes wOuLd Be mUCh hARdeR tO rEAd.

Capital letters make it much easier for people to read and understand what you write. In particular, they show where a new sentence begins.

When to use capitals

- At the beginning of a sentence
- For a person's name
- For days, months and special occasions (e.g. Hallowe'en)
- For place names (e.g. Limerick)
- For titles of books, TV shows, films (e.g. *The Hunger Games*)
- For names of companies (e.g. Ryanair)
- For specific organisations (e.g. RTÉ)
- When writing about yourself ('I').

Written work

Re-write the following sentences correctly, using capital letters where necessary.
(The first one is already done for you.)

1. are you going to galway on saturday?

   <u>Are you going to Galway on Saturday?</u>

2. have you got a map, laura?

3. spain and italy are both european countries.

4. what are you getting for christmas?

5. mr smith laughed at rory.

6. paris is the capital of france.

7. where are joe and billy going?

8. the thames river is in london.

9. rté is showing the match in croke park on sunday.

10. i have just finished reading.

Written work

Re-write the following paragraph correctly, using capital letters where necessary.

we had seen an ad for the circus in the local newspaper, the daily herald. when we reached it, we found it was really busy. lots of people bumped into us, including a small man who was searching for his lost dog. he kept calling out for trixie, and pushing past us. my friend bobby said that he was very rude. then some kids we knew from st mark's school also started shouting. i suppose they thought they were being funny. inside the big top, we were surrounded by rows and rows of people waiting expectantly for the show to begin. bobby and i were just as excited as we waited for coco the clown to appear.

End Punctuation

Without end punctuation a person reading your work wouldn't know when you had finished a sentence they wouldn't know if you were asking them a question or if you were just making a statement sentences without end punctuation would be very annoying to read

Sentences need to finish with the correct punctuation mark. More often than not, end punctuation consists of a full stop (.). Question marks (?) and exclamation marks (!) are also necessary at specific times, so it is important to know when to use them for someone reading your work to know exactly what you mean.

Full stops

Full stops go at the **end** of ordinary sentences and are the most common end-of-sentence punctuation mark.

> In the United States, a 'full stop' is also known as a 'period'.

Examples:

If it rains, remember to bring an umbrella.

On Sunday, we went for a walk in the park.

When the doorbell rang, Mary just ignored it.

Question marks

A question mark shows that the sentence is a **direct question** and **expects an answer**.

Examples:

What time did you arrive in school this morning?

Can you send me a text later?

Do you know where my bag is?

Exclamation marks

An exclamation mark shows **feeling** and **emotion** and is used for sentences **giving orders** or **portraying strong sentiments**.

> Exclamation marks exclaim!

Examples:

Be careful! It's very hot!

Don't eat all my sweets!

Great! The exams are finished and I'm free!

Written work

Re-write the following paragraph correctly, using capital letters and the correct end punctuation marks where necessary.

last saturday i went to dublin zoo i saw elephants, bears and tigers i ate a delicious lunch in the restaurant the best thing about the whole day was going to the gift shop i bought several books about endangered animals i can't wait to go again

Written work

Re-write the following sentences using the correct end punctuation marks.

1. What is your date of birth
   _____

2. Lucy came second in the race
   _____

3. Close the window right now
   _____

4. My dad made a sandwich
   _____

5. Beyoncé is a fantastic singer
   _____

6. What time is it
   _____

7. Let's all go to the zoo
   _____

8. Who wants to go to the cinema
   _____

9. Matthew has just fallen off his bike
   _____

10. Call an ambulance at once
    _____

Learning Outcomes

I have studied the rules for capital letters and end punctuation.

- All sentences begin with a capital letter.
- Capital letters help us to see clearly where new sentences begin.
- Proper nouns (the names of people, places and organisations) all start with capitals.
- Full stops go at the end of statements.
- Question marks show that a sentence is a question.
- Exclamation marks show strong emotions.

Student signature _____ **Date** _____

» Sentences

A sentence is a group of words that forms a complete thought. Sentences make statements, ask questions or give commands.

Examples:

I am hungry. (*statement*)

Are you going home? (*question*)

Sit down. (*command*)

A sentence must **make sense** standing on its own.

As we have seen, it begins with a **capital** (uppercase) **letter** and ends with an **end mark**: a full stop (.), question mark (?) or exclamation mark (!). Writing your thoughts and ideas down in complete sentences makes it easier for someone reading your work to understand what it is you want to say.

- Ordinary sentences tell you something. They end with a full stop. (.)
- Questions ask something. They end with a question mark. (?)
- Exclamations are sentences that show emotion. They end with an exclamation mark. (!)

Written work

Correct the following sentences by re-writing each one with capital letters and ending marks.
(The first one is already done for you.)

1. where did you go for lunch today

   <u>Where did you go for lunch today?</u>

2. we have maths after lunch

   _____

3. will you bring your friend to my house after school

   _____

4. we cannot use the gym

   _____

5. what i can't believe it

   _____

Written work

Proofread and re-write the following passage so that it will make sense for the reader. Form sentences using capital letters and end marks.

> To proofread something means to read over it and check it for mistakes and omissions.

i had walked too far i looked at the strange houses the street light came on i looked around to see if i recognised anything then i realised that i was lost i saw a curtain flicker suddenly in the window of a big house i knocked on the front door to get directions a man opened the door he smiled as he ushered me inside i turned round he was gone just then i heard a key turning in a lock

_____

_____

_____

_____

_____

_____

_____

_____

_____

Verbs and Subjects in Sentences

A sentence must have a **verb** (an action word). The **subject** of a sentence is 'who' or 'what' is doing the action.

Written work

Re-write the following, underlining the verb in each sentence.

(The first one is already done for you.)

1. I like Fridays.

   I _like_ Fridays.

2. I want a new smartphone for my birthday.

   _____

3. John needed to do well in his exams.

_____

4. I am happy.

_____

5. Are you going to the show?

_____

6. Don't be silly!

_____

Written work

Re-write the following, underlining the subject in each sentence.

1. The boy was sick.

_____

2. The weather is awful today.

_____

3. When will you come?

_____

4. They knew they were caught.

_____

5. I am so sorry.

_____

6. It looks bad for her.

_____

Simple Sentences

A simple sentence **makes one statement**, **asks one question** or **gives one command**.

Examples:

I am Irish. (*statement*)

Will you go to the big match tomorrow? (*question*)

Do it! (*command*)

There are **four types** of simple sentences.

1. The subject is something, e.g.

   I am sick.

2. The subject does something, e.g.

   The class behaved badly

3. Someone does something to someone or something, e.g.

   The dog bit the postman.

4. The subject of the sentence gives the impression of being something, e.g.

   The girl seems to be happy.

Verb Agreement

The verb in the sentence must **'agree'** with the subject.

If there is **one single subject** in the sentence, the verb must agree with it.

The man shouts.

So the man – a single subject – shouts. He shouts, not 'He shout'.

A plural subject has a verb in the plural form.

The men shout.

So the men – plural subject – would shout, they wouldn't 'shouts'!

This seems obvious to us, as we are so used to these simple sentence constructions. It would not sound right to us to say, 'The man shout' or 'The men shouts'. But consider this sentence written in two ways, one of which is incorrect:

> *The rhythm of the pounding waves is calming.*
>
> *The rhythm of the pounding waves are calming.*

Here it might be difficult to figure out should we use 'is' or 'are'. Is 'rhythm' that has to agree, or 'waves'? In this instance, we need to make the **subject** (*rhythm*) and the **verb** (*is*) agree, even though there are other words intervening (*the pounding waves*). It is the rhythm that is calming – the rhythm just happens to come from the waves.

> *The rhythm* [of the pounding waves] *is calming.* ✔

Additionally ...

Collective nouns are singular, so they have a verb which is singular.

The *flock* of sheep *climbs* the mountain. (*The flock climbs*)

Two subjects have a plural verb.

John and *Susan write* to us regularly. (*They write to us*)

Written work

Re-write the following sentences, choosing the correct form of the verb to complete them.
(The first one is already done for you.)

1. The programmes (*was, were*) very enjoyable.

   *The programmes **were** very enjoyable.*

2. The dog (*barks, bark*) loudly.

   _____

3. The birds (*sing, sings*) every morning.

   _____

4. He (*is, are*) tall.

   _____

5. The car and train (*go, goes*) very fast.

   _____

Compound Sentences

A compound sentence **links two things**.

A compound sentence is formed when you join two longer phrases with a conjunction, such as *and, but, or, not, so, yet, then*, e.g. Aidan can be rude at times, *but* he is a nice boy.

Compound sentences can specify a **contrast**, **reason**, **place**, **purpose** or **time**.

Examples:

I like this one *although* I also like that one. (*contrast*)

I entered the competition *because* I thought I could win. (*reason*)

I looked *where* I knew I would find the book. (*place*)

Mary put food out for the birds *so that* they would not go hungry. (*purpose*)

Tom went *before* he could be caught. (*time*)

Written work

Re-write the sentences below and identify if they are simple or compound.

(The first one is already done for you.)

1. We ate lunch.

   We ate lunch. **Simple**

2. The rocket flew high, but soon fell to the ground.

3. What is your favourite joke?

4. The party was great fun, yet few had bothered to come.

5. We went to the movies.

6. She speaks fluent Russian although she lives in Ireland.

Written work

Re-write the following sentences, underlining the conjunctions in each.

(The first one is already done for you.)

1. It rained all day so the children remained indoors.

   It rained all day <u>so</u> the children remained indoors.

2. Although I bought a ticket in the raffle, I did not win.

3. She spoke as if she knew everything.

4. I was terrified in case the snake escaped.

5. The builders started early so that they would finish on time.

6. We thought he was rich, whereas he was actually very poor.

Written work

Re-write the following sentences, choosing the correct conjunction from the bracket to complete them.

1. Should I go to the party (*but, or*) stay at home?

   _____

2. I put on my hat and coat (*because/so that*) it was cold.

   _____

3. I combed my hair (*before/because*) I went to school.

   _____

4. I answered the phone (*as soon as/until*) it rang.

   _____

5. Patrick was not tired (*yet/and*) he had to go to bed.

   _____

6. It has been three weeks (*so that /since*) I saw you.

   _____

Written work

Re-write the sentences below, choosing the best conjunction from the list to join the two short sentences together.

if, although, as, because, but

(The first one is already done for you.)

1. The rug was very expensive. It had been woven by hand.

   The rug was very expensive as it had been woven by hand.

2. The show went ahead. The lead singer was unwell.

   _____

3. She wanted to bake cupcakes. She had run out of flour.

   _____

4. He decided to visit the gym more often. He wanted to get fit.

   _____

5. Keep the protective clothing on. You don't want to be stung.

   _____

Learning Outcomes

I have studied different types of sentences.

- A sentence makes a statement, asks a question or gives a command.

- A sentence begins with a capital letter and ends with a full stop, question mark or exclamation mark.

- A simple sentence does one thing.

- A compound sentence is a sentence that has two parts linked by a connecting word or words.

Student signature   **Date**

» Paragraphs

A paragraph is a section of text or prose writing. It is usually a group of sentences about the same topic. There are no rules about the length of paragraphs – they may be long or short.

What is 'prose'?

Prose is the name we give to writing and language that has no formal metrical rhythm or structure.

Normal, everyday speech is spoken in prose and most people think and write in prose form. This book, for example, is written in prose! Think of it as the opposite of poetry, which is often structured and rhythmic.

The Importance of Paragraphs

Paragraphs are very important. They help you to organise your writing and make it easy to read.

Paragraphs usually have one **topic sentence** (often at the start) which gives the main idea of what you are writing about.

Example:

I had such a good time at my cousin Lizzie's party. Her mum organised loads of games and I won two prizes. There were all types of food to eat – sweet and savoury. I probably ate too much cake and ice-cream. Afterwards, Lizzie opened her presents and her dad gave us all more birthday cake. It was great fun … But my tummy still feels a little queasy.

In this case, the opening sentence (the topic sentence) gives the **main point** of the idea and all the other sentences are **details** about this idea.

Written work

Re-write the following short paragraph. Then underline the topic sentence.

Our dog is playful. He spends most of the day running around the back garden chasing any bird he sees. When I throw sticks, he gets really excited and fetches them. If visitors come to our house, he always rushes out to greet them. He enjoys it when they pat him. On trips to the beach, he loves to splash about in the water. Charlie is a very playful pet.

_____

_____

_____

_____

_____

_____

_____

Organising Your Writing Using Paragraphs

Paragraphs **break up** your writing into easy-to-read sections.

They are used to indicate the **beginning of a new point or idea** when you are discussing something. If you are writing a short story, paragraphs can be used to:

- Introduce a new character
- Change the location or setting
- Introduce new dialogue
- Change the mood or atmosphere
- Go back in time (flashback).

> Roddy Doyle is a very well-known and popular Dublin author. He has written many books for children and young adults, including _A Greyhound of a Girl_ and _Her Mother's Face_.

Written work

Re-write the following text (taken from **Brilliant** by Roddy Doyle), inserting paragraphs where you think they should go.

Gloria, Raymond and Ernie ran to the corner as fast as they could, even though they were probably running towards danger. But the Black Dog had gone. He'd disappeared. They could look down four streets from here. There was no sign of the Dog – no sign of anything. It was cold, a kind of moving cold, like a freezing, invisible animal was rubbing against them. "Well," said Ernie, and he pointed at both streets across from their corner. "He can't have gone down there. We'd have seen him crossing the road." The cold crawled around them. There was no sound now from the wind. "This one," said Raymond, and he pointed left. "Come on."

_____

_____

_____

_____

_____

_____

_____

_____

_____

_____

_____

_____

Learning Outcomes

I have studied paragraphs.

- A paragraph is a piece of writing about a similar point or topic. Paragraphs can be long or short.
- Paragraphs space out your work and make it easier to read.
- The topic sentence is the main point of a paragraph.
- A new paragraph is made to indicate a new point being made, a change of topic, mood or speaker.

Student signature _____   **_Date_** _____

» Commas, Semi-Colons and Colons

Commas, semi-colons and colons are common and very useful punctuation marks. It is important to know when and how to use them.

The Many Uses of Commas

A comma (,) is a common punctuation mark that has **a number of different uses.**

> Comma is a Latin word that means 'a piece cut off'.

Most commonly, in prose writing, commas are used to **indicate a short pause**, breaking up the sentence to indicate how it might sound if spoken aloud. They are used to make the meaning of a sentence clear by separating its different parts.

But commas are also very important in ensuring that sentences give the **meaning as intended** by the writer. Consider the importance of the comma in the following sentence:

Let's eat, Grandma!

Here, we take it to mean that a grandchild is talking to his grandmother, and saying that it's time for them to tuck in.

Now consider:

Let's eat Grandma!

This puts an altogether different spin on things, making the reader wonder what Grandma did to deserve being eaten!

So, commas are very important in helping to establish the correct meaning in sentences. They are also used for the following purposes:

- **To separate items in a list**

Apples, oranges, blueberries and bananas are good for you.

- **To indicate a pause or interjection**

The teacher, Mr. Murphy, came in early.

- **In compound sentences, to indicate two or more parts**

Daniel watched a movie, but Sarah read a book.

- **In direct speech**

"Let's go soon," Daniel said.

- **To separate introductory words**

Well, I'd prefer to go to the park.

- **To break up large numbers**

The company was in debt to the tune of €300,000,000.
(Notice the comma is placed after every three digits, reading from the right.)

- **When opening and closing letters**

Dear Mr. Murphy, … Yours sincerely,

- **When writing about towns and counties**

I live in Drogheda, Co. Louth.

> Notice a comma is not used before 'and' in the list. In the United States, however, they prefer to put in a comma. It is called the 'Oxford comma'.

There are lots of instances in which we use commas. Like full stops, they are a very common punctuation mark.

Written work

Re-write the following sentences correctly, placing commas in the correct positions.

1. Take a break will you!

   Take a break, will you!

2. Once upon a time a prince fought a great battle.

3. Of course we must go.

4. However I would like to go early.

5. It was here according to Diarmuid the accident happened.

6. He lost €200000000 in a shaky deal.

Written work

Re-write this passage correctly, a piece from **The Cay** by Theodore Taylor, by adding in capital letters, commas and full stops.

> Theodore Taylor was an American author of books for young adults, of both fiction and non-fiction. *The Cay* took him only three weeks to write and went on to sell millions of copies all over the world.

it was very hard to finish my breakfast because i wanted to go to punda the business district the oldest part of town and then to fort amsterdam where i could look out to see if there was an enemy u-boat out there i wanted to see it and join the people in shaking a fist at it

Semi-Colons

A semi-colon (;) is a punctuation mark used to indicate a longer pause in a sentence than a comma.

A semi-colon **links two sentences** that are closely connected and relate to each other, making them into one. They can also be used to **replace conjunctions** (*and*, *but*, *or* etc.).

> As you can see, the semi-colon symbol consists of a full stop above a comma – so the pause is slightly longer than a comma but slightly shorter than a full stop.

Written work

Re-write the following pairs of sentences as one using the semi-colon.

(The first one is already done for you.)

1. The bus hadn't arrived. I was going to be late for school.

   The bus hadn't arrived; I was going to be late for school.

2. The hotel was closed. The river had flooded it.

3. The ambulance took a long time to come. There was a traffic jam on the M50.

4. All the staff was sick. They had eaten the curry.

5. His car wasn't worth much. The brakes didn't work.

6. Some students go to school by bus. Some go by car.

Colons

A colon (:) is a punctuation mark used **to introduce** a list, a title, a quotation or direct speech.

Examples:

To make the perfect mashed potatoes, you need three things: butter, salt and potatoes!

Martin Luther King famously said: 'I have a dream.'

A colon can also be used to **introduce** a statement or a definition of something.

Examples:

I know what I'm going to do: I'm going to hide!

Puffin: a seabird of northern and Artic waters, with a large head and brightly coloured beak.

Written work

Re-write the following sentences using a colon where appropriate.

(The first one is already done for you.)

1. Students going on the school trip to Barcelona should bring the following their passport, comfortable shoes, one bag and an umbrella.

   Students going on the school trip to Barcelona should bring the following: their passport, comfortable shoes, one bag and an umbrella.

2. The first line of the poem is "Let us go then, you and I".

3. Mum turned round from the cooker and asked "Are you going somewhere, Dearbhla?"

4. I need to get the following a turkey, Brussels sprouts, stuffing, potatoes and carrots.

5. The title of the song is "Imagine".

6. Dad remarked "Is that the outfit you are wearing to the school dance?"

Learning Outcomes

I have studied the rules for commas, semi-colons and colons.

- A comma has many different uses, but most commonly it marks a short pause in a sentence.
- A semi-colon marks a slightly longer pause in a sentence, as well as linking two related sentences.
- A colon is used to introduce a list, a title, a statement, a quotation or direct speech.

Student signature _____ *Date* _____

» Apostrophes

An apostrophe (') is a punctuation mark used to show ownership or to indicate missing letters.

Showing Ownership

Examples:

The *girl's* coat was too big (*singular* – the coat belonging to the girl).

The *boys'* bags were left in a heap (*plural* – the bags belonging to the boys).

It is important to notice that the apostrophe comes **before** the letter 's' when talking about singulars (the one coat belonging to the one girl) and **after** the letter 's' when talking about plurals (the many bags belonging to the boys).

Indicating Missing Letters

Examples:

We'll go tomorrow (*We will*).

Don't tell me what to do (*Do not*).

It is important to notice here that the apostrophe is placed **exactly** where the letter/letters are left out (*we'll* – the 'wi' in 'will' is left out; *don't* – the 'o' in 'not' is left out) and the space between the words is then closed up.

Apostrophes are also used with **years**, **letters** and **numbers** (though this might not always be the case – some newspapers and books take on different styles and might prefer to leave apostrophes out).

Examples:

He was a teenager in the 1980's.

Mind your p's and q's.

3's are lucky numbers.

You'll also see apostrophes used in people's **surnames**.

Examples:

Denis O'Murchu

Mary O'Donoghue

When writing about **time**, apostrophes save us from having to say, for example, 'four of the clock'.

Example: We have tea at four o'clock.

Written work

Re-write the following sentences correctly, using the apostrophe to show ownership in all the underlined words.

(The first one is already done for you.)

1. The teacher entered the <u>boys</u> names in the register.

   The teacher entered the boys' names in the register.

2. The <u>babys</u> howl was heard in the next street.

   _____

3. My <u>mothers</u> cooking is the best in the world.

   _____

4. Mr <u>Tierneys</u> house is larger than Mr <u>Murphys</u>.

   _____

5. The <u>Boy Scouts</u> hall is very big.

   _____

6. Sarah and <u>Joans</u> cat is missing.

   _____

Written work

Re-write the following sentences to merge two words into one using an apostrophe.

(The first one is already done for you.)

1. All is well that ends well.

   <u>All's well that ends well.</u>

2. We have a new car.

   _____

3. You are not a good student.

   _____

4. Sheila came at six of the clock.

   _____

5. That team will not win the championship.

_____

6. Do not be silly.

_____

Its and It's

These two words are frequently confused.

Its means 'belonging to it'.

Example: The cat licked _its_ paw (the paw belonging to it).

It's is a short form of the words 'it is', where the apostrophe is used to indicate the omission of the letter 'i' in 'is'.

Example: _It's_ raining cats and dogs (it is raining cats and dogs).

Written work

Re-write the following sentences, replacing 'its' with 'it's' where necessary.

(The first one is already done for you.)

1. Its snowing in Dublin.

   <u>It's snowing in Dublin.</u>

2. How old are its pups?

   _____

3. Remember its the shortest day on 21st December.

   _____

4. Its lovely to walk along the river.

   _____

5. If its open for business, I will go in and buy something.

   _____

6. The river broke its banks.

   _____

Learning Outcomes

I have studied the apostrophe.

- An apostrophe has a number of different uses.
- It is used to show ownership.
- It is used to show that letters are missing.
- It is used with years, letters and numbers.
- It is used in surnames.
- It is used in the telling of time.

Student signature _____ **Date** _____

» Dialogue and Quotation Marks

Dialogue

Dialogue is what we call **direct speech** in novels.

Dialogue reports the exact words of the character. Writers use direct speech in fiction to let the reader **hear** what the characters have to say for themselves. This helps to **reveal** what characters are like and can also add **drama** to the story.

Quotation Marks

Quotation marks ("/") **show when someone is speaking**.

They are placed at the **beginning** and **end** of what someone has said.

Example:

"We will win this game," said Joe.

"I don't think we will," replied Deirdre.

> Quotation marks are also known as inverted (upside-down) commas or speech marks.

Punctuation is used in this way so the reader can easily follow a conversation in written work. (A lot of the time you'll see the double quotation mark ("/") used in to do this job, but some writers and newspapers prefer to use single quotation marks ('/') – it's just a matter of preference.)

Reading work

Read the following dialogue from the novel **_The Last Guardian_**, the eighth book from the _Artemis Fowl_ series by Eoin Colfer.

> Eoin Colfer was a primary school teacher before he became a full-time writer for children and young adults. The _Artemis Fowl_ series has sold over 20 million copies worldwide.

Argon snagged a stack of cards from his file.

"I am going to show you some inkblots, and you tell me what the shapes suggest to you."

Artemis's moan was extended and theatrical.

"Inkblots. Oh, please. My life span is considerably shorter than yours, Doctor. I prefer not to waste valuable time on worthless pseudo-tests. We may as well read tea leaves or divine the future in turkey entrails."

"Inkblots are a reliable indicator of mental health," Argon objected.

"Tried and tested."

"Tested by psychiatrists for psychiatrists," snorted Artemis.

Argon slapped a card down on the table.

"What do you see in this inkblot?"

"I see an inkblot," said Artemis.

"Yes, but what does the inkblot suggest to you?"

Artemis smirked in a supremely annoying fashion.

"I see card five hundred and thirty-four."

"Pardon me?"

"Card five hundred and thirty-four," repeated Artemis, "of a series of six hundred standard inkblot cards. I memorised them during our sessions. You don't even shuffle."

So in this piece, we know exactly when Artemis Fowl is talking, and when Dr Argon is talking. Sometimes, the author doesn't even indicate who has spoken after each sentence, e.g. "What do you see in this inkblot?" We know intuitively here that it is Dr Argon who has just spoken, because the author starts every new piece of dialogue on a new line (and also, we read Artemis replying in the next sentence). We can also come to our own conclusion as to what sort of character Artemis Fowl is, by what he says and the way he says it. By using dialogue, the author develops the character.

Written work

Write five sentences in the space provided below which, in your opinion, describe Artemis.

(The first one has been started for you.)

1. I think Artemis is extremely ...

2.

3.

4.

5.

Dialogue Structure

Take a new line for every change of speaker. If there are only two speakers, when it is established who they are, they do not have to be named all the time; just start their next sentence on a separate line.

Example:

"Hey Gerry," said Anne excitedly, "what do you think of my smartphone?"

"It's really cool. Do you've any apps on it?" Gerry inquired.

"I've loads of apps! Do you want to see some of them?"

"Sure do! I'm getting a new phone for Christmas."

> ## Note!
> The comma after the last word of a section of direct speech is put inside the quotation marks. If you are using a question mark (?) or an exclamation mark (!), it is also put inside the quotation marks.

Written work

Re-write the following examples of dialogue using the correct punctuation.

1. are you having a nice day mary asked.

_____

2. no i hate Mondays complained diarmuid.

_____

3. i really love Mondays mary replied.

_____

4. i hate Mondays, school and homework diarmuid sighed.

_____

5. what about Tuesdays asked mary.

_____

Written work

Write about ten lines of dialogue between two friends, Jan and Paul, who are arguing about which film they should see in the cinema at the weekend.

(The first two lines are done for you.)

> "Are you going to the cinema on Saturday?" asked Paul.
>
> "Sure am. There's a great romance film on," replied Jan.
>
> _____
>
> _____
>
> _____
>
> _____
>
> _____
>
> _____
>
> _____
>
> _____
>
> _____

Punctuating Split Speech

If the dialogue is split by a verb (such as *said*), then you should punctuate it like this:

"I don't care," said the student, "the teacher should not have given us piles of homework at the weekend."

A comma comes after the word 'care' and after the word 'student'. The next piece of direct speech is put into new quotation marks and the full stop is put inside them.

Written work

In this piece of dialogue from William Golding's book, **Lord of the Flies**, most of the punctuation has been removed. There are no quotation marks, commas, full stops or question marks for the conversation between the three marooned boys. As a result, the extract is very hard to read.

Use the space below to re-write the extract, putting in punctuation where you think it should go to make the conversation between Piggy, Ralph and Jack clear for the reader.

> William Golding was best known for this book, *Lord of the Flies*, and though it was not popular when it first came out – actually it was allowed to run out of print – it went on to become a best-seller and is now considered a classic.

Piggy looked up miserably from the dawn-pale beach to the dark mountain

Are you sure Really sure I mean

I told you a dozen times now said Ralph we saw it

D'you think we're safe down here

How the hell should I know

Ralph jerked away from him and walked a few paces along the beach Jack was kneeling and drawing a circular pattern in the sand with his forefinger Piggy's voice came to them hushed

Are you sure Really

Go up and see said Jack contemptuously and good riddance

No fear

The beast had teeth said Ralph and big black eyes

He shuddered violently Piggy took off his one round of glass and polished the surface

What are we going to do

_____

_____

_____

_____

_____

_____

_____

_____

_____

_____

_____

_____

_____

_____

_____

_____

_____

_____

Written work

This next excerpt is from **Buddy** by Nigel Hinton. Buddy and his dad are having a conversation. This time all the punctuation marks are missing. It is very frustrating to read. Rewrite the extract in the space below, adding capital letters, full stops, commas, quotation marks and question marks as necessary to make the passage easily understood.

> Nigel Hinton is an English writer. The character of Buddy was originally supposed to be a nine-year-old called Stuart.

he washed up the plates made a cup of tea for his dad and then went up to bed he felt warm and sleepy after the food he was already dozing off when he heard the door open you asleep nearly not yet buddy sat up his dad was standing near the doorway his face was in shadow there was a long silence then his dad said we do all right don't we you and me course we do yeah well he took a couple of steps into the room and then turned as if he was about to go out again I'm glad about the job he wanted his dad to stay I got all worried tonight what about don't know stupid things I thought something might have happened accident or something you won't get rid of me as easy as that his dad said and laughed

Learning Outcomes

» Brackets, Dashes and Hyphens

Some punctuation marks – such as brackets, dashes and hyphens – help you get natural pauses into your writing.

Brackets

Brackets are used in **pairs** and **enclose additional information** to show that it is separate but related to the sentence around it.

> Brackets are also known as parentheses (say: *par-n-th-sees*).

Example: Clodagh arranged to meet us on her birthday (6th March) outside the cinema.

Brackets are also useful for **separating definitions or explanations** from the rest of the sentence.

Example: The UN (United Nations) was established in 1945.

Written work

Re-write the following sentences, putting in the missing brackets.

(The first one is already done for you.)

1. My uncle an adventurous sort of man decided to buy a motorbike.

   My uncle (an adventurous sort of man) decided to buy a motorbike.

2. The Eiffel Tower found in Paris is a major tourist attraction.

   _____

3. Sydney Opera House built at the entrance to Sydney Harbour is also famous.

   _____

4. Ireland has been in the EU European Union for over forty years.

_____

5. Jack's shoes made of expensive leather were all scuffed and dirty.

_____

6. George Washington the first US president was born in 1732.

_____

7. Mount Everest 8,848m is the world's highest mountain.

_____

8. Laura and Jamie who are actually first cousins both have red hair.

_____

Dashes

The dash is often used to **separate an afterthought**.

Two dashes may be used in a similar way to brackets to **separate** an additional piece of information within a sentence.

Example: My teacher – an unpredictable character – took up skydiving.

A **single dash** can be used to add a **dramatic pause** in a sentence.

Example: Everyone thought Aunt Clare was generous – until it came to birthdays.

Written work

Re-write the following sentences, putting in the missing dashes.

(The first one is already done for you.)

1. You are the one friend the only one who offered to help me.

   You are the one friend – the only one – who offered to help me.

2. My neighbour a strange lady eats bacon and banana sandwiches.

   _____

3. Sinead never complained about anything at least that was her opinion.

   _____

4. Uncle Ben made such a fuss about washing the car typical!

   _____

5. The two builders Pete and Bruce were very fond of long tea-breaks.

_____

6. I had always liked apple crumble until that weekend when I ate too much of it.

_____

7. The letter dated April 20th arrived on May 7th.

_____

8. We only wanted one gerbil but the salesman talked us into buying four hamsters.

_____

Hyphens

Hyphens are used to **join words** (or parts of words) **together**.

Examples:

Some pets seem only _half-intelligent_.

We love eating _ice-cream_.

> A hyphen is half the length of a dash, with no spaces either side of it.

You should also hyphenate all **compound numbers** from _twenty-one_ through to _ninety-nine_.

Example: There are _twenty-six_ very lively pupils in our class.

> A prefix is what we call a word or letters that can be placed at the start of another word to change its meaning.

Hyphens are also used when **attaching a prefix** to most proper nouns (those with capital letters).

Example: Natalie is _half-French_.

> ### Remember!
> Hyphens link words to make the meaning clear.
> Example: 'We saw a huge man-eating tiger in the zoo.'
> Without the hyphen, this sentence would have a very different meaning!

Written work

Re-write the following sentences, putting in all the missing hyphens.

(The first one is already done for you.)

1. Everyone agrees that Charlie is a friendly looking dog.

   *Everyone agrees that Charlie is a **friendly-looking** dog.*

2. The hottest time of the year is in mid July.

   _____

3. Our new neighbours have a two year old child.

   _____

4. We are studying pre Victorian history.

   _____

5. Our new puppy is now completely house trained.

   _____

6. More than two thirds of the class love reading.

   _____

7. The firemen decided to reenter the burning building.

   _____

8. Mum insists on sugar free drinks.

   _____

Learning Outcomes

I have studied the use of brackets, hyphens and dashes.

- Brackets, hyphens and dashes can be helpful in creating pauses in your writing.

- Dashes and brackets do much the same thing – they add extra information.

- They should not be over-used, as overuse of brackets and dashes can make your writing look disjointed.

- The main sentence must make sense without the extra words inside the brackets.

- Hyphens link words and help to make your writing clear.

Student signature   ***Date***

» Handwriting

"The quick brown fox jumps over the lazy dog."

Used to practise handwriting since 1888, "The quick brown fox jumps over the lazy dog" is what is known as a pangram (from the Greek, meaning 'every letter'), a sentence or phrase that contains all the letters of the alphabet.

The Importance of Good Handwriting

Although most of us enjoy using text and email to communicate, good handwriting is still essential for school work and examinations. Being able to write neatly and clearly enables you to get your ideas down on paper quickly, as well as making it easy for a teacher or examiner to read what it is you have to say (and not be frustrated by poor handwriting!). We also write birthday and Christmas cards, letters of thanks or apology, and it is a great skill to be able to do so with good, distinctive handwriting.

Be smart! Practise your handwriting!

- Good handwriting helps in every part of the school curriculum.

- Taking notes and producing handwritten essays is easier when you have good handwriting.

- Neat handwriting means that words cannot be misunderstood.

- Writing carefully by hand will help you develop accurate spelling and punctuation.

- Clear handwriting gives others a positive impression – which can help in tests and examinations.

Take a look at some of the signatures of the most famous names in the world.

Victor Hugo

Beyoncé

Abraham Lincoln

Oprah Winfrey

Harper Lee

Queen Elizabeth I

Elvis Presley

Barack Obama

Jane Austen

Madonna

Benjamin Franklin

Oliver Cromwell

Rembrandt

Michael Jackson

Martin Luther King Jr

Edgar Allan Poe

Bill Gates

Marilyn Monroe

Written work

In your opinion, which signature gives the most positive impression? Give a reason.

_____

_____

_____

_____

In your opinion, which signature gives the least positive impression? Give a reason.

_____

_____

_____

_____

Yours truly ...

Your own signature is important. Whether you plan on becoming famous one day or just want to have a signature that you like, it's worth experimenting and practising until you get it right.

Written work

Practise writing your signature in the spaces below.

_____

_____

_____

Tips for good handwriting

- Write with a pen that is comfortable to use.
- Try varying your handwriting to find a style you like (everyone's handwriting is distinctive to them).
- Don't rush your writing.
- Distinguish capital letters from small letters.
- Be careful with letters that go through the line: f, g, j, p, q, and y.

- Keep practising the letters you have trouble with.
- Cross every t.
- Dot every i and j carefully.
- Practise connecting letters.
- Aim to produce legible, neat work, using joined-up writing.

Written work

Using your best handwriting, copy the following paragraph (taken from *Brilliant* by Roddy Doyle) into the lines below.

Gloria Kelly lay in bed. She was wide awake. She knew her brother, Raymond, was too. She could tell by the way he was breathing. It was awake breath. He was lying there, thinking and listening. Sleep breath was different. It was longer and lighter. It was less in and out.

Written work

Using your neatest handwriting, copy this short passage from the novel, **Of Mice and Men**, by the American author, John Steinbeck.

John Steinbeck is one of the greats of American fiction writing and his works are considered classics in western literature. Many of his books have been adapted into films, including *Of Mice and Men*, *The Grapes of Wrath* and *The Red Pony*.

It was Sunday afternoon. The resting horses nibbled the remaining wisps of hay, and they stamped their feet and they bit the wood of the mangers and rattled the halter chains. The afternoon sun sliced in through the cracks of the barn walls and lay in bright lines on the hay. There was the buzz of flies in the air, the lazy afternoon humming.

Written work

Re-write the following extract (taken from **Jurassic Park** by Michael Crichton) in your best handwriting.

Michael Crichton was an American author best known for his science fiction and thriller books. He is the only creative artist to date ever to have his works simultaneously charting at No. 1 in US television, film and book sales (with *ER, Jurassic Park and Disclosure*).

Grant did the only thing he could think to do. He ran forward and jumped up, throwing himself against the body of the dactyl. He knocked it onto its back on the ground, and fell on top of the furry body. The animal screamed and snapped; Grant ducked his head away from the jaws and pushed back, as the giant wings beat around his body. It was like being in a tent in a sandstorm. He couldn't see; he couldn't hear; there was nothing but the flapping and shrieking and the leathery membranes.

Learning Outcomes

I have studied the importance of good handwriting.

- Neat, distinctive handwriting is important across all subject areas. It ensures that what you write can be read clearly and accurately.

- Writing clearly and legibly leaves a good impression.

- Everyone's handwriting is distinctive to them.

Student signature

Date

Teacher's initial

Section 3 – Spelling

A good understanding of spelling will make you a much better writer, reader and all-round communicator. Accurate spelling helps readers to understand what you write.

» General Rules

Improving Your Spelling

- There is no substitute for reading widely. Watch out for new words and their spellings when you do so.

- Keep a record of tricky words or words you find difficult. Put a dot next to words you look up in your dictionary. If you look it up more than once, write it down in your list.

- Sounding out words by syllables can often help. Make sure that you are pronouncing words correctly. This can help you to avoid some common spelling errors, such as canidate instead of can*did*ate, or libary instead of lib*rar*y.

- Use a dictionary or spellchecker (but don't rely on spellchecker as it can miss errors, especially when you have used the wrong word but have spelled it correctly.)

- Use mnemonics (say: *nem-on-ics* [you don't pronounce the 'm' at the beginning]): mnemonics are memory devices or tricks which you can make up yourself to help you with tricky words. For example, there are three 'e's' in c**e**m**ete**ry, which is the sound you make when you scream – eee! And you pull a**par**t to se**par**ate.

Homophones

Homophones are words that **sound the same** but **mean different things**.

'Homophone' is from the Greek and means 'same sound'.

Example: I always try to *write* the *right* answer.

There, Their, They're

Commonly misused homophones are: *there*, *their* and *they're*.

- We use **there** when writing about *place* (*There she is! Over there!*)

- The word **their** is about *possession and belonging* (*The students keep their pens in their desks.*)

- **They're** is short for *they are*. (*It looks like they're all half-asleep.*) Here, the apostrophe is used to indicate the missing letter 'a' in 'are'.

Written work

Re-write the following sentences, choosing the correct homophone.

(The first one is already done for you.)

1. The nurse gave the students (*there*, *their*, *they're*) injections.

   The nurse gave the students **their** injections.

2. Our footballers think (*there*, *their*, *they're*) going to win the match.

   _____

3. Suzie is sure that (*there*, *their*, *they're*) are no mistakes in her work.

   _____

4. I wonder if (*there*, *their*, *they're*) going bowling tonight.

   _____

5. Rob hid a secret stash of chocolates over (*there*, *their*, *they're*).

   _____

6. Look at the big silly smiles on (*there*, *their*, *they're*) faces.

   _____

Synonyms

Synonyms are words that have a **similar meaning**.

Synonyms are used to add variety to your writing. They help you avoid using the same word too often.

Examples:

New is another word for *modern*.

Pal is another word for *friend*.

Written work

Re-write this passage using synonyms for the repeated underlined words. Choose the correct synonym from the list.

stood, good, sat, climbed, lovely, walked, great

(The first one is already done for you.)

I went to the park. I went on the swings. I went on the slide. It was nice when I went on the roundabout. It was a nice, sunny day. I like when the weather is nice.

I walked to the park.

_____

_____

_____

_____

_____

Antonyms

Antonyms are words which are **opposite in meaning**.

Examples:

Thin is the antonym of *fat*.

Full is the antonym of *empty*.

Written work

Re-write the sentences below, choosing the correct antonym.

(The first one is already done for you.)

1. a) .... here, and tell me all about it.

   b) .... at once and raise the alarm.

   Antonyms: *Come, Go*

   a) Come here and tell me all about it.

   b) Go at once and raise the alarm.

2. a) The .... is only what we can change.

b) The .... cannot be altered.

Antonyms: *past, present*

a) _____

b) _____

3. a) The .... man was sentenced.

b) The .... man was set free.

Antonyms: *guilty, innocent*

a) _____

b) _____

4. a) The cup of tea was too .... because it had three sugars.

b) The boy grimaced at the .... taste of the lemon.

Antonyms: *sour, sweet*

a) _____

b) _____

5. a) The student was .... for his good behaviour.

b) The driver was .... for his dangerous driving.

Antonyms: *praised, criticised*

a) _____

b) _____

6. a) The lost puppy was ....to be seen.

b) This Christmas it snowed ....

Antonyms: *everywhere, nowhere*

a) _____

b) _____

Words ending with -ible or –able

Words ending with 'ible' or 'able' sound just the same, so sometimes it is hard to know the correct spelling. There is no easy rule – you just have to learn the spellings!

-IBLE

These are some words that end in *-ible*:

horrible, terrible, responsible, invincible, possible, incredible, edible, reversible, sensible, indestructible

Written work

Re-write the sentences choosing the correct *-ible* word.

(The first one is already done for you.)

1. The h .... boy tries to bully everyone.

   The **horrible** boy tries to bully everyone.

2. A t .... storm battered the island.

   _____

3. There were two p .... answers to the question.

   _____

4. The science fiction film had i .... special effects.

   _____

5. This strange food is not e ....

   _____

6. The jacket had a r .... lining.

   _____

7. This new plastic bottle is supposed to be i ....

   _____

8. The r .... captain had a well-disciplined squad.

   _____

9. The s .... thing to do was to stop.

   _____

10. The mighty hurling team was i ....

    _____

-ABLE

These are some word that end in *-able:*

reliable, enjoyable, probable, valuable, adorable, miserable, amiable, breakable, respectable, disposable

Written work

Re-write the sentences choosing the correct *-able* word from the list above.

(The first one is already done for you.)

1. The r............ tractor always started.

   The reliable tractor always started.

2. The two girls decided to be a .... and bury their differences.

   _____

3. Put those d .... cans in the trash bin.

   _____

4. The b .... china was stored carefully in the cabinet.

   _____

5. Everyone was gloomy because of the m .... weather.

   _____

6. The little, fluffy dog was a ....

   _____

7. When he failed his driving test he was taught a v.................. lesson.

   _____

8. The p .... score is a draw.

   _____

9. A half-day's holiday is always e ....

   _____

10. Her aunt thought it r .... to wear a hat in church.

    _____

Using ie and ei

Sometimes it is difficult to remember whether a word is spelled with *ie* or *ei*. There is a very simple rule about this:

> Use i before e
> except after c

General Rule	Examples
Use i before e (*when the sound is e*)	believe, brief, diesel, chief, field, grief, hygiene, niece, piece, priest, relief, thief
Except after c	ceiling, deceive, receipt, receive
Usually write ei (*when the sound is other than e*)	foreign, heir, heifer, height, leisure, neighbour, reign, sleigh, their, vein, veil, weight, weird

> ### Remember!
> There are always exceptions to the rule: e.g. mischief, species, friend, ancient

Written work

Re-write the following sentences correctly, using the correct spellings.

(The first one is already done for you.)

1. I just had to eat a second (*peice, piece*) of delicious cake.

   *I just had to eat a second **piece** of delicious cake.*

2. Little Damien is quite a (*mischeivous, mischievous*) child.

   _____

3. Look at that huge spider on the (*ceiling, cieling*).

   _____

4. We gave our (*nieghbour, neighbour*) a fright yesterday.

   _____

5. I can't (*beleive, believe*) that Joan is so (*conceited, concieted*).

   _____

6. Sometimes it's better to (*recieve, receive*) than to give!

   _____

» Commonly Confused Words

Some words can be tricky!

Lose and Loose

Lose: a verb, meaning 'to not win' or 'to misplace something'.

Example: Don't *lose* your pocket money.

Loose: an adjective, meaning 'not tight'.

Example: My shoelaces are *loose*.

Written work

Re-write the following sentences, using the correct word.

(The first one is already done for you.)

1. Joe's tooth is (*lose, loose*) and he's afraid he'll (*lose, loose*) it.

   <u>Joe's tooth is **loose** and he's afraid he'll **lose** it.</u>

2. The screw has just come (*lose, loose*) on the door handle.

   _____

3. My new clothes seem slightly (*lose, loose*).

   _____

4. Patrick's football team always seem to (*lose, loose*) at home.

   _____

5. If your spellings are correct, you won't (*lose, loose*) marks in the exam.

   _____

6. Julie needs to buy a big purse for all her (*lose, loose*) change.

   _____

Your and You're

Your: pronoun meaning 'something belonging to you'.

Example: I think *your* food is getting cold.

You're: contraction, short for 'you are'.

Example: I don't know what *you're* talking about.

Practise and Practice

Practise: verb meaning 'to prepare'.

Example: John should *practise* the guitar at home.

Practice: noun meaning 'preparation'.

Example: We have basketball *practice* tonight.

Affect and Effect

Affect: verb meaning 'to influence'.

Example: Lack of sleep can *affect* your health.

Effect: noun meaning 'result'.

Example: Lack of sleep has an *effect* on your health.

Principle and Principal

Principle: noun meaning 'fundamental idea, rule or belief'.

Example: It is the basic *principle* of law that someone is innocent until proven guilty.

Principal: adjective meaning 'main or most important'; principal can also be used as a noun leading on from this adjectival meaning, as in the principal of a ballet company, or the principal of a school.

Examples:

I think our school has the best *principal*!

Dublin is Ireland's *principal* city.

> ### Tip!
> An easy way to know which spelling to use is to always remember that the princi**pal** is your **pal**!

Stationary and Stationery

Stationary: adjective or adverb meaning 'fixed in one place and not moving'.

Example: The car had been *stationary* since the battery died.

Stationery: collective noun for paper, envelopes, pens, etc.

Example: You will find extra copy books in the *stationery* cupboard.

> ## Tip!
> An easy way to know which one to use is to remember that
> station**e**ry means **e**nvelopes.

Written work

Re-write the following sentences using the correct words.

1. I hope (*your, you're*) happy with the gifts you got.

   _____

2. Is it true that (*your, you're*) kitten keeps chasing birds?

   _____

3. Our new teacher likes to (*practise, practice*) yoga.

   _____

4. Tomorrow's music (*practise, practice*) has been cancelled.

   _____

5. What (*affect, effect*) did the bad weather have on you?

   _____

6. Did flooding (*affect, effect*) the school sports day?

   _____

7. She wrote in her journal every day on (*principle/principal*).

   _____

8. The (*principle/principal*) of our school is retiring this year.

   _____

9. He wanted new (*stationary/stationery*) for his letter-writing.

_____

10. The airplane remained (*stationary/stationery*) on the runway for over an hour.

_____

Tricky Spellings to practise

argue   argument   beautiful   beginning   believe
business   completely   definitely   develop   different
disappear   disappointment   exaggerate   excellent   experience
February   forty   friend   generous   guarantee   humour
humorously   independent   immediately   interesting   interrupt
justice   knowledge   language   library   literature   memory
necessary   neighbour   opinion   prefer   quiet
quite   responsible   separate   surprise
tomorrow   tragedy   truly
unfortunately   vicious
Wednesday   weird

» Plurals

Plural means more than one of something or other.

Adding 's' or 'es'

Most plurals are really easy. Singular nouns (a noun that names only one thing) can be made plural by just adding *s* to the end. Nouns ending in 'x', 'z', 's', 'sh' and 'ch' form the plural by adding *es* to the end.

Written work

Add either an *s* or an *es* to the end of each word to form the plural.

1. book _____
2. school _____
3. fox _____
4. case _____
5. eyelash _____
6. church _____
7. break _____
8. apple _____
9. kitten _____
10. guitar _____
11. pizza _____
12. crash _____
13. computer _____
14. lunch _____
15. pet _____
16. movie _____
17. car _____
18. beach _____
19. wish _____
20. class _____

Written work

Write a complete sentence that has both a singular noun and a plural noun in it.

e.g. The *panda* is one of the world's most lovable *animals*.

1. _____
2. _____
3. _____
4. _____
5. _____

Tricky Plurals

For words that end with a 'y'

Just add *s* for words where the second-last letter is a vowel:

toy ➡ toys

essay ➡ essays

For words where the second-last letter is a consonant, change the final 'y' to 'ies':

baby ➡ babies

party ➡ parties

Written work

Write in the plural of the following words by adding either *s* or *ies*.

1. key _____	2. story _____
3. boy _____	4. dictionary _____
5. lady _____	6. reply _____
7. pony _____	8. guy _____
9. celebrity _____	10. theory _____

Learning Outcomes

I have studied some of the main spelling rules.

- Homonyms have the same spelling and pronunciation but have different meanings.
- Synonyms are words that are similar in meaning.
- Antonyms are words which are opposite in meaning.
- Use 'i' before 'e' except after 'c'.
- There are exceptions to all the rules!
- Some spellings are tricky and just have to be learned.

Student signature _____ **Date** _____

Teacher's initial _____

Section 4 – Imaginative Language: Prose, Poetry, Fiction & Drama

» Prose and Poetry

Writers have a way with language. Prose writers and poets all use language in distinctive ways to ensure that they communicate effectively with their readers.

Prose

As mentioned earlier, prose is the name we give to writing and language that has no formal metrical rhythm or structure. Prose is **ordinary language** as used in **everyday speech**. It is commonly found in newspapers, magazines and textbooks, as well as in fictional writing.

Prose writers – sports journalists, for example – have to create images for people of the event they have witnessed and now have to report on, to ensure that the reader gets as much of a flavour as possible of the event from only the words on the page. In prose writing, writers constantly strive to use **imagery** (word pictures) to help the reader imagine the scene they are describing, e.g.

On a balmy Sunday in September, the fans file into Croke Park, a riot of colour, eagerly anticipating what is sure to be an exhilarating and closely contested All-Ireland Final.

Everything we read is either non-fiction or fiction. Non-fiction is based on fact; fiction comes from the imagination.

'e.g.' is an example of an abbreviation (the word 'abbreviation' is from the Latin *brevis*, meaning 'short'). This abbreviation, e.g., means 'for example', coming from the Latin phrase *exempli gratia*. **Example:** 'The cafe provided all sorts of treats, e.g. fresh fruit, smoothies, truffles and numerous desserts.'

Other abbreviations you'll often come across are:

- 'i.e.', meaning 'therefore' or 'in other words', from the Latin *id est* ('that is ...'): 'The service charge is included in the bill, i.e. you don't need to leave a tip';

and

- 'etc.', from the Latin *et cetera*, meaning 'and the rest', used to indicate further similar examples without having to name them all (or used if the other examples are too boring to name!): 'I sometimes shock my parents by clearing the table, doing the dishes, cleaning my room, etc.'

Written work

Imagine you are a sports journalist reporting on a team that has not been performing well this season, but which has suddenly improved. Write a report (a short paragraph) using some of the words listed below to guide you.

poor results, criticism, pressure, newspaper article, disappointed supporters, embarrassing defeats, courage, strong attack, overwhelming victory

(The first sentence has been started for you.)

United has come under severe pressure this season ...

Poetry

Poets have a very particular way with language. Poetry is one of the most interesting and imaginative ways writers have of expressing their thoughts and feelings. Poets choose every word and punctuation mark carefully, to help express what it is they want to say to their audience. Poetry uses **imaginative language** to express feelings and ideas, arranging words in special and sometimes intricate **patterns**.

Prose explains, but poetry sings.

Subject matter

Writers choose a topic to write about. Poems can be about **characters**, **places**, **events**, **conflict** or **feelings**. Another name for the subject matter is **theme**. Some poems tell stories. These narrative poems tend to be quite long and often rhyme. Many poets choose nature for their subject matter, e.g. William Wordsworth in his famous poem, 'Daffodils':

> William Wordsworth was an English poet of the eighteenth/ nineteeth century. This poem is one of his most popular and loved, with his simple yet evocative depiction of nature.

I wandered lonely as a cloud
That floats on high o'er vales and hills,
When all at once I saw a crowd,
A host, of golden daffodils;
Beside the lake, beneath the trees,
Fluttering and dancing in the breeze.

Written work

Look at the lines below from the poetry of Seamus Heaney. Re-write the quotations and say what the subject matter is in each case. Choose from the following list:

nature, a person, a place, a feeling, conflict

(The first one is already done for you.)

> Seamus Heaney is one of Ireland's greatest poets, indeed considered the most important Irish poet since W.B. Yeats. He won the Nobel Prize for Literature in 1995. He died in 2013.

---

1. "Sometimes, leather-aproned, hairs in his nose, /He leans out …"

   Sometimes, leather-aproned, hairs in his nose, /He leans out" (a person)

2. "He stood up, shifted the baton-case /Further round his belt …"

   _____

3. "So that the ocean on one side is wild/ With foam and glitter …"

   _____

4. "And here is love/ like a tinsmith's scoop …"

   _____

5. "Our unfenced country/ Is bog that keeps crusting …"

   _____

6. "Stockinged corpses/ Laid out in the farmyards …"

   _____

Style

Every writer has their own way of using language – a particular **style**. Poets use imaginative language to express feelings and ideas. A writer's own feelings are shown by the **tone** (the kind of voice) they use. For example, it's clear that this poet does not like homework. We can see this through the choice of words:

> Homework sits on top of Sunday, squashing Sunday flat
>
> Homework has the smell of Monday …

(From 'Homework' by Russell Hoban)

> Russell Hoban was an American writer who lived in England for much of his life. He wrote exclusively for children for a decade, and this poem comes from a series of seven picture books featuring Frances, a lively girl who gets into a lot of mischief.

We can see that the poet uses special ways (or **techniques**) to write about his chosen subject matter and to convey his message. He compares his subject to other things. In this second example, the poet is telling readers that the season of winter puts on a performance and transforms things with a covering of snow:

> Winter is the king of showmen,
>
> Turning tree stumps into snow men …
>
> (From 'Winter Morning Poem' by Ogden Nash)

> Ogden Nash was an American poet who was known for his humorous writing. He wrote over 500 pieces of comic verse.

Here the poet makes use of **dramatic imagery** to paint a picture of winter in the reader's mind.

Reading work

Find Ogden Nash's poem 'Winter Morning' online and read it to see some great winter imagery.

Rhyme and Imagery

Poets enjoy experimenting and 'playing' with words. Some poems **rhyme** (use words with the same sound) and have a regular beat (rhythm). Others use **free verse**, where picking up a rhythm can be challenging and it is up to the reader to really concentrate and examine the words being used by the poet. Poems are often divided into shorter sections, called **stanzas**, which can make them easier to read. (In songs, the different sections are known as 'verses', with the repeated section falling between them being called the 'chorus'.)

Written work

Write descriptive sentences for each of the following ideas, using an interesting image of your own.

(The first one is already done for you.)

1. a great save

   The goalkeeper caught the ball with hands of steel.

2. an angry man

   _____

3. a beautiful sunset

   _____

4. a scary sight

   _____

5. a loud noise

   _____

Metaphors

A metaphor is a word or phrase used to describe something as if it were something else.

Example: A *great wave of terror* suddenly washed over the young child.

This comparison is an imaginative way of describing the child's feelings.

Written work

Re-write the following short poem ('What is the Sun' by Wes Magee), underlining all the metaphors that you can find.

> Wes Magee is a poet and children's author from Scotland. He was a teacher when he first began writing poems, after a student of his complained that there were no dinosaur poems – so Wes decided to write one for him!

What is the Sun?

The sun is an orange dinghy
sailing across a calm sea.

It is a gold coin
dropped down a drain in heaven.

It is a yellow beach ball
kicked high into the summer sky.

It is a red thumb-print
on a sheet of pale blue paper.

It is the gold top from a milk bottle
floating on a puddle.

Similes

A simile compares one thing with another using the words 'like' or 'as'.

Examples:

The eel moved *like a ripple on the water*.

Big Joe was *as angry as a mad bull*.

Written work

Add a simile of your own to each of the following sentences.

(The first one is already done for you.)

1. When the bell rang, the class ran out *like a herd of wild elephants.*

2. The noise in the corridor was like

3. The tyre was as flat as

4. The bus is as slow as

5. My friend swims like

6. The crowd at the match screamed like

7. The little puppy was as good as

8. The school bag was as heavy as

9. My sister is as sweet as

10. My older brother is as strong as

Written work

Imagine you are a space explorer who has just discovered alien life on a distant planet. You have to send a report of what you have seen back to your base on earth. Write seven sentences below describing an alien, using similes. You have to report what he looks like, smells like, how tall he is, how strong he is, how fast he is, how he walks, what he sounds like. Help everyone back at home to really see what you can see!

(The report is already started for you.)

Report 3/3 from Space Explorer 227XZ. Date: 5th January 2050

On 5th January at 12 noon earth time, I saw the first alien on this planet. He was as green as ……… He smelt like ………… He was as tall as ………… He seemed to be strong as ……………… He was as fast as …………… He walked like ………… He sounded like ………
This concludes my report on the sighting of an alien. Over and out!

_____

_____

_____

_____

_____

_____

_____

_____

Improving Similes

If you want to show that a classmate is noisy, you could use a simile and write, 'Barry is as noisy as an elephant'. By using **exaggeration**, however, you can improve this comparison by writing, 'Barry is as noisy as a whole herd of angry elephants'.

Written work

Re-write the following sentences using new similes of your own.

1. His locker was as smelly as old socks. Yuck!

_____

2. I am as busy as a bee.

_____

3. Argh! This computer is as slow as a snail.

_____

4. The school bus is as packed as a tin of sardines.

_____

5. My drink is as cold as ice.

_____

Written work

Read the following poem by Moira Andrew and write a short personal response saying what you like or find interesting about it.

Balloon Fiesta

Apostrophes of the air,
they soar like bubbles
making speech marks
in the evening sky.
Their colours blossom
into zigzags, spirals, stripes,

as they dip down spinning
across paper-light fields.
When dragon-fires roar
they rise, punctuating
the sky in a matrix
of disappearing dots.

'Matrix' means changing pattern.

_____
_____
_____
_____
_____
_____
_____
_____
_____
_____
_____
_____
_____

Learning Outcomes

I have studied the language of prose and poetry.

- Prose is ordinary language as used in everyday speech.

- A theme is the subject matter of a poem.

- Style is the particular use of language.

- The tone is the kind of voice used.

- Writers use imagery to paint word pictures for their readers.

- Poets often use comparisons (similes and metaphors) to make their writing more colourful and interesting.

Student signature

Date

» Fiction

Fiction refers to literature (novels and short stories), drama and film scripts. Such narrative writing is imagined by the author (it is a work of fiction, not of fact).

"You take people, you put them on a journey, you give them peril, you find out who they really are."

(Joss Whedon)

Plot

Plot refers to what happens in a fictional story.

It is the **storyline** or the pattern of events that makes the reader curious to know what will happen next.

There is no story without conflict.

e.g. Harry learns Professor Snape is after the Sorcerer's Stone. The Professor lets loose a troll, who nearly kills Harry and his friends. Harry finds out that Hagrid let out the secret of the giant dog to a stranger in return for a dragon. Now Snape can reach the Sorcerer's Stone.

(Synopsis [say: *sin-op-sis* – a brief summary] of *Harry Potter and the Sorcerer's Stone* by J.K. Rowling)

> J.K. Rowling was living in a small flat with her young son when she first started writing about Harry Potter. It went on to become one of the most popular children's books of all time. Her second name is pronounced 'Rolling', not 'Rau-ling'!

Character

A character is usually a **person** in the story.

Writers try to make their characters as interesting as possible. The reader needs to be able to **see** (through **word pictures**) the character.

e.g. 'The face of Elrond was ageless, neither old nor young, though in it was written the memory of many things both glad and sorrowful. His hair was as dark as the shadows of twilight … his eyes were grey as a clear evening.' (From *Lord of the Rings: The Fellowship of the Rings* by J.R.R. Tolkien)

The character will have an aim or goal. This provides **conflict**. Depending on the type of person the character is, the goal will be achieved successfully or not. On this journey, the character will change and learn. A character's personality is shown by what they say, what they do and what others say about them.

Dialogue

Dialogue, also known as **direct speech**, brings the story to life.

It tells us about the character. How the character speaks is also introduced in many ways, e.g. *shouted, replied, answered, whispered, warned, insisted, cried*, etc.

Written work

Read the following extract of dialogue from **Buddy** by Nigel Hinton.

Choose an adjective from the list to describe Buddy.

clever, secretive, tough, happy

Underline the piece of dialogue which suggests this adjective.

> "I told you about those yesterday," Mr. Normington said, pointing at his jeans. "You said it was only while your mother was repairing your jeans."
>
> "Yes, sir."
>
> "Well?"
>
> "She hasn't done them yet," Buddy said …
>
> "Why not?"
>
> For a moment Buddy wanted to tell him, wanted to shout,
>
> "Because I haven't seen her for five months – that's why."
>
> That would soon shut him up.
>
> "I don't know, sir."

Setting

The setting is the **world** of the story, where and when the action takes place.

Writers use the **five senses** to describe this world. The setting also contributes to the **mood** of the story.

Written work

Read the following extract from **The Hobbit** by J.R.R. Tolkien.

Choose two of the senses he uses in his description from the list.

John Ronald Reuel Tolkien was an English writer and poet world-famous for his classic high fantasy works *The Hobbit* and *The Lord of the Rings*.

seeing, hearing, smelling, tasting, touching

Underline the phrases in the passage which suggested these senses.

> In a hole in the ground there lived a hobbit … it was a hobbit-hole and that means comfort. It had a perfectly round door like a porthole, painted green, with a shiny yellow brass knob in the exact middle. The door opened on to a tube-shaped hall like a tunnel: … provided with polished chairs, and lots and lots of pegs for hats and coats – the hobbit was fond of visitors.

Problems/Obstacles

Obstacles **prevent** the character from reaching their goal.

They test the character and cause them to change and learn, increasing the **tension** and **excitement** in the story for the reader.

Written work

Read the following extract from **The Cay** by Theodore Taylor.

Choose a problem or an obstacle from the list which occurs in the passage.

mountain, volcano, storm, earthquake

Re-write the extract, underlining the piece of text which suggests this obstacle.

> Soon, I felt water around my ankles. Then it washed to my knees. It would go back and then crash against us again. Timothy was taking the full blows of the storm, sheltering me with his body. When the water receded it would tug at us, and Timothy's strength would fight against it.

_____

_____

_____

_____

Climax

'Climax' refers to the **tension** in a story.

This tension rises to the high point, the **climax**, where a decision has to be made to act or not to act. The crisis has to be resolved.

Written work

Read the following amended extract from **Lord of the Flies** by William Golding.

Simon has arrived at Roger's party, which has begun to go out of control. He wants to tell them his news. The boys are playing out the hunt of the pig earlier that day.

Write five sentences to explain what you think is happening.

> A thing was crawling out of the forest. It came darkly, uncertainly. The shrill screaming that rose before the beast was like a pain …
>
> *"Kill the beast! Cut his throat! Spill his blood!"* …
>
> Simon was crying out something about a dead man on a hill.
>
> *"Kill the beast! Cut his throat! Spill his blood! Do him in!"*

The sticks fell ... The beast was on its knees, in the centre, its arms folded over its face. It was crying out against the abominable noise something about a body on a hill. The beast struggled forward, broke the ring and fell over the steep edge of the rock to the sand by the water.

_____

_____

_____

_____

_____

Resolution

'Resolution' refers to the story's problems and loose ends being **resolved**.

The character has succeeded or failed in achieving their goal. To have a successful resolution, the ending must be believable within the world of the story, leaving the reader satisfied.

> ### Tip!
> When writing your own stories, aim for a lively conclusion. A poor ending would be: 'Then we went home', or 'Then she woke up and realised it was all a dream!'

Written work

Read the following (very) short story and rate its ending good, bad or excellent. Write two sentences explaining why or why not you were satisfied.

'She was on her own, in the dark. She reached out for the matches on the table. They were put into her hand.'

Rating:

_____

Reasons:

_____

_____

_____

Learning Outcomes

I have studied the language of fiction.

- The plot or storyline is what happens in a fictional story.

- A character is a person in the story.

- Dialogue is used to show what characters actually say. It brings the story to life.

- The setting is the world of the story.

- Obstacles prevent characters from reaching their goal.

- The climax or high point of the story is when the tension is at its most exciting and where a character has to make an important decision.

- The resolution refers to how the story's problems and crises are resolved.

Student signature

Date

» Drama and Film

Drama and film are both story-based art forms. Drama comes from the Greek word for action and usually refers to plays intended for live performance on stage before an audience. Film is a story or event recorded by camera as a set of moving images and played on a screen.

"Drama is life with the dull bits cut out."

(Alfred Hitchcock)

Drama is similar to fiction in that there is usually a plot, characters, action, conflict, climax and resolution. Drama is different to fiction because, in a play or film, we can actually see and hear the characters and the action. We see where the action is taking place (the set). We hear sound effects and music. This brings us into the 'world' of the story.

Plays

Plays are a form of literature, with scripted dialogue written by a playwright, performed by actors on stage in front of an audience.

Play Script

A play script is the dialogue and stage direction for a play.

- Characters' names are written on the left.

- A new line is given each time a different character speaks.

- There are no speech marks.

- There is no use of 'he said'/'she said'.

- Stage directions are used for actions. They can be in brackets or italics after a character's name. They are also used to describe the set.

Example:

This is part of the description of the set in Act One Scene One of the play **Sive** *by John B. Keane:*

> The kitchen is poorly furnished, with an open hearth on its left wall. A door leads to a bedroom at the left side of the hearth. On the wall facing the audience there is a small window, and a door leads to the yard at the front of the house …

Set

The set creates the world of the story through scenery, props (small objects, such as a book or a weapon, which can be carried on stage), lighting and sound effects.

These add to the atmosphere of the story. The playwright describes this in their stage directions.

Written work

Read the following adapted stage directions from **Juno and the Paycock** by Sean O'Casey and choose three words from the list below to describe this world.

> Seán O'Casey was a world-renowned Irish dramatist who wrote about Dublin's working classes, amongst other topics. His works continue to be performed on stage to this day.

> The living room of a two-room tenancy occupied by the Boyle family in a tenement house in Dublin. Between the window and the dresser is a picture of the Virgin and a crimson bowl in which a votive light is burning. There is a small bed, a galvanised bath, a teapot and a frying pan on a table, a few books and a long-handled shovel.

well-off, poor, religious, cramped, comfortable, orderly, educated, careless

The Boyle family is ...

Stage Directions

The writer also uses stage directions to show actors how to act in a particular scene.

They are in brackets or italics after a character's name.

Written work

Read the following extract from **The Field** by John B. Keane. Underline the stage directions and choose one of the words from this list to describe the atmosphere created.

> John B. Keane was one of Ireland's best-loved playwrights. From Co. Kerry, his plays were often inspired by his locality. This play, *The Field*, was adapted into a film.

happy, tense, calm, quiet, exciting

The Bull McCabe, a local farmer, has been renting a field from Maggie which she has sold against The Bull's wishes.

Maggie: You've no claim.

Bull: [dangerously] Look out for yourself, you! Look out for yourself. [He cows the old woman]

Bull: That field is mine! Remember that! I'll pay a fair price. God Almighty! 'Tis a sin to cover grass and clover with concrete.

[Maggie Butler rises and moves towards the doorway]

Maggie: [To Maimie] I'll have to be goin' – there's no-one in the house but myself.

Bull: You should remember that!

[Maggie looks back, startled]

In my opinion, this scene is ...

Film

"Movies took you right up to the edge but kept you safe."

(John Updike)

Film has plot, characters, setting, dialogue, conflict, climax and resolution, like fiction and drama. But it has one extra ingredient: the camera. The director of the film chooses what you see by how they use the **camera**. The director places the character, the setting and the position of these in the frame of the shot. This influences the viewer's response to the story. **Colour, music** and **sound effects** are also used to sway the viewer's feelings while the film is being watched.

Character

In film, as in theatrical drama, the character is shown by action, facial expression, tone of voice, costume and gesture.

We can hear and see the character, just like a character in a play. But the director of a film will decide where the character is placed in the shot. If the character is to appear powerful, the director puts the camera down low so that the character appears huge in the frame. If the character is to be seen as weak, the camera is positioned above the character so that they are seen as small and vulnerable.

Example:

A director explaining how she created a weak character for her film:

'I told the actor to keep looking down, to talk in a whisper and to walk with a slight stoop. I positioned the camera high to emphasise his vulnerability.'

Written work

Imagine a tense scene from a film. The hero has just arrived in town, which has been taken over by a dangerous gang of criminals. If you were to direct this scene, what advice about facial expression, tone of voice and gesture would you give the actor playing the hero? Where would you position the camera for this shot?

If I were to direct this scene, ...

_____

_____

_____

_____

Setting

The setting of a film, like a drama or novel, is the world of the story.

Directors take great trouble presenting this world to their audience through background, colour, lighting and props. The viewer must believe in the world of the film for the story to work.

Example:

A director explaining how he created the set for his fantasy film:

'I wanted to create a world which was not realistic, so I shot a background of huge trees using CGI. I used a very bright green sky and had no shadows. I used oversized props so that the characters seemed very small.'

> CGI is an acronym (say: *a-kro-nim*) of 'Computer Generated Imagery' (and an acronym is an abbreviation formed from the first letter or letters of a phrase or word!).

Written work

Imagine you are directing a film set in space. How would you suggest this to the viewer using background, colour, lighting and props?

If I were to direct a film set in space, ...

_____

_____

_____

_____

Music and Sound Effects

Music and sound effects are used by directors to create a particular atmosphere in the world of their films.

Soft, gentle music gives a calm mood, while loud, shrill music suggests conflict and tension.

Example:

The director of the famous scary movie, *Jaws*, Steven Spielberg, made great use of sound effect to build tension for the audience. He and composer, John Williams (world-famous for his musical scores) used the sound effect of gentle lapping water which then changed to threatening, lower-pitched musical sounds to create the suggestion of a dangerous predator lurking beneath the waves.

Written work

The director wants to create a mood of conflict in his fantasy film. What type of music and sound effects would you suggest to the director to achieve this effect?

I would suggest ...

Learning Outcomes

I have studied the language of drama and film.

- A drama is a story presented on stage or on television.

- The plot of a play involves characters who face a problem or conflict.

- Plays are meant to be performed for an audience.

- Play scripts include the dialogue to be spoken by the actors as well as stage directions.

- Sets, lighting, costumes and props transform a theatre stage into the 'world' of the play.

- Film allows the viewer to hear and see the story.

- The camera is the extra ingredient in making a film.

- The director often shows what a character is like by the angle of the camera.

- The setting of a film makes its world real for the viewer.

- Music and sound effects create the mood in a film.

Student signature

Date

Teacher's initial

» Self-Assessment

Overview of My Literacy Skills

Areas I know well. Place a tick (✔) in the box provided.

Areas I need to revise. Place a (✘) in the box provided.

Grammar		Punctuation		Spelling		Prose, Poetry, Fiction & Drama	
Nouns	❑	Capital letters	❑	General Rules	❑	Subject matter	❑
Pronouns	❑	End punctuation	❑	Commonly confused words	❑	Style	❑
Articles	❑	Sentences	❑	Plurals	❑	Rhyme and imagery	❑
Adjectives	❑	Paragraphs	❑			Metaphors	❑
Verbs	❑	Commas	❑			Similes	❑
Adverbs	❑	Semi-colons	❑			Plot	❑
Conjunctions	❑	Colons	❑			Character in fiction	❑
Prepositions	❑	Apostrophes	❑			Dialogue	❑
		Dialogue and quotation marks	❑			Setting	❑
		Brackets	❑			Problems / Obstacles	❑
		Dashes	❑			Climax	❑
		Hyphens	❑			Resolution	❑
		Handwriting	❑			Play script	❑
						Set	❑
						Stage directions	❑
						Character in drama	❑
						Setting	❑
						Music and sound effects	❑

» Key Literacy Terms

adjective	a word that describes a noun, e.g. **hot** coffee, **lazy** lions.
adverb	a word that describes a verb, e.g. whisper **softly**, walk **slowly**.
apostrophe	looks like this ' and is used to show **missing letters** and **belonging** (ownership: possessive apostrophe).
brackets	look like this ( ) and often used to separate **additional information** in a sentence.
clause	a group of **related words** containing a subject and a verb. A main clause is a simple sentence, e.g. 'Ruth gave me her address'. Subordinate clauses do not stand alone, e.g. 'although she is a very private person'.
colon	looks like this : and used mainly to introduce **a list**.
comma	looks like this , often separates items in a list and joins clauses.
conjunction	a word linking two sentences or two parts of a sentence, e.g. **however**, **and**. Conjunctions are also known as 'connectives'.
consonant	any letter that is not a vowel.
dash	looks like this – a long line punctuation mark used before adding **extra information** or to introduce **a pause**.
direct speech	**actual words spoken** by someone.
grammar	the **structure** and **rules of a language** used to make meaning clear.
homophone	a word that sounds the same as another, but has a different meaning, e.g. **there** and **their**.
hyphen	looks like this - a short line punctuation mark **used to join parts** of some compound words, e.g. sister-in-law, mix-up.
literacy	the **ability to read**, **write** and **speak**, so as to communicate effectively.
noun	a word that **names** something, e.g. Emily, chocolate, happiness.
phrase	usually two or more **related words** within a sentence, e.g. in the afternoon.
prefix	letters that can be placed at the start of a word to change its meaning, e.g. **un**sure.
preposition	a word that shows how things are related, e.g. **in**, **at**, **along**.
pronoun	a word that can be used instead of a noun, e.g. **I**, **you**, **it**, **they**.
semi-colon	looks like this ; and is sometimes used to separate long **lists** or to **join sentences**.
speech marks	look like " " and are often called **inverted commas**. They are used to show direct speech.
synonym	a word with the same or similar meaning of another word, e.g. **funny**, **humorous**, **hysterical**.
syntax	the **order of words** in a sentence.
verb	a doing or action word, e.g. I **talk**, you **walk**, she **leaves**.
vocabulary	all the **words** of a language.
vowels	a, e, i, o, u

»Index